921
Ste

WILKIE, Katharine   1421

Robert Louis Stevenson

Lakeside Joint School Dist.
19621 Black Road
Los Gatos, Ca. 95030

ROBERT LOUIS STEVENSON

Storyteller and Adventurer

Robert Louis Stevenson:

ILLUSTRATED BY ANTHONY D'ADAMO

Storyteller and Adventurer

KATHARINE WILKIE

1421

HOUGHTON MIFFLIN COMPANY · BOSTON

NEW YORK · ATLANTA · GENEVA, ILL. · DALLAS · PALO ALTO

Contents

The Land of Counterpane

When I was sick and lay a-bed,
I had two pillows at my head,
And all my toys beside me lay
To keep me happy all the day.

And sometimes for an hour or so
I watched my leaden soldiers go,
With different uniforms and drills,
Among the bed-clothes, through the hills;

And sometimes sent my ships in fleets
All up and down among the sheets;
Or brought my trees and houses out,
And planted cities all about.

I was the giant great and still
That sits upon the pillow-hill,
And sees before him, dale and plain,
The pleasant land of counterpane.

A Child's Garden of Verses

CHAPTER 1

Make-Believe

The little boy in the large four-poster bed was very busy. Before him on the snowy counterpane (bedspread) were dozens of lead soldiers. There were foot soldiers, men on horseback, and a few generals in full dress uniform. There were toy cannons and supply wagons.

A fierce battle was raging. At one side of the bed were some long ships in which the boy's favorite army could escape if it had to.

But he did not think the army would have to escape. After all, *he* was directing the battle from where he lay back against his pillows. He was a master at the game of make-believe.

Once he gave a sharp cough. His mother looked anxiously into the bedroom.

"Do you think his cold is worse?" she asked his nurse, Cummy.

"I hope not," Cummy answered. "I have given him his medicine. I have kept him warm. I have seen that he is quiet — as quiet as anyone can keep Master Lou. If he had his way, he would never be still a minute."

Little Robert Louis Stevenson did not hear a word they said. By now the battle was fast and furious. He moved troops from one spot to another. He had men charging up the hills in the bedclothes. His dark eyes shone with excitement. At last he clapped his hands.

"My soldiers captured the fort!" he croaked hoarsely.

Cummy looked at him with concern. She saw that his cheeks were red.

"You do play so hard, laddie," she said. "How do you feel, Master Lou?"

"My head hurts," he said. "Please tell me a story, Cummy."

"There's just time before supper," his

nurse said. She smoothed his rumpled pillows and straightened his wrinkled sheets. Then she sat down by his bed.

"What shall it be?" she asked. "Giants? Goblins? Dragons? A princess in distress?"

Louis thought for a minute. Then he shook his head. "Not this time. I think I'd like to hear about Joseph and his brothers."

Cummy smiled at him. She was a fisherman's daughter. She had been brought up in a humble Scottish home where the children knew the Bible almost by heart. Alison Cunningham (Cummy's real name) thought The Book, as she called the Bible, had the best stories in the whole world.

Robert Louis Stevenson loved her as though she were his own mother. He thought she told the best stories he had ever heard. He smiled up at her.

"Long ago in Palestine, there lived a man with many sons," she began. "But the son nearest his heart was named Joseph . . ."

The youngster in the bed never took his eyes from her face. In his mind he went with

Joseph every step of the way as Cummy told how the boy of olden days roamed across the fields in search of his brothers who were tending their sheep.

Lou almost held his breath as he heard how the jealous brothers planned to kill their father's favorite. He pictured Joseph sold as a slave to a band of traders going to Egypt. He saw the Hebrew boy rise to favor. He saw him accused falsely and thrown into prison. Then he watched him again as he grew to be second in rank to the ruler of all Egypt.

Cummy told how Joseph's brothers came years later from faraway Canaan to ask for grain. She recounted how Joseph, now a prince of Egypt, pretended to keep his young brother Benjamin as a hostage.

Her voice shook with feeling as she brought the story to an end. "I am Joseph, your brother, whom you sold into slavery, but do not be afraid. I forgive you for everything. Go home and bring our father to me. God must have planned it all this way."

10

Louis gave a deep, happy sigh. "I think you are wonderful, Cummy. I never get tired of your stories."

He glanced out the window. It was growing dark outside. He almost bounced in his excitement.

"It's nearly time for Father to be home!" he shouted. "May I put on my clothes now? Please say yes."

She hesitated. The doctor had said he might get up for his evening meal, but she thought he looked feverish.

"I suppose you may," she agreed. "If we are going out for a walk tomorrow, you had better get the feel of being up and about tonight."

Louis had hardly put on his jacket and trousers before he heard his father's steps on the front stairs. In another moment, Thomas Stevenson was in the room.

"Smoutie?" he called.

He held out his arms. The little boy ran to him.

"I don't know whether I want to be called

11

'Smoutie' (*smoh' tee* — little salmon) or not," he told his father. "I'd rather be a soldier."

The big man laughed. Then he held him at arm's length.

"What's this I hear about a cough and a cold?" he demanded. "You look well enough to me."

"I am well," Louis announced. He coughed hoarsely as he spoke.

His mother, who had just come into the room, looked over her son's head at Cummy. The two women shook their heads slightly at each other.

"Of course you are well," his father told him. "And you are growing. A few more years, and you will be building lighthouses with me."

"I'm not sure I'd like that," Louis told him.

"You'll like it," his father said firmly. "My father was a lighthouse builder. My brother David and I are lighthouse builders. Someday you will follow in our footsteps. I

13

can't imagine a Stevenson not being a light-house builder."

"What must a lighthouse builder know?" Louis asked.

"He must know the sea and the seacoast," Thomas Stevenson answered. "There are hundreds of miles of Scottish seacoast which must have lighthouses. I could draw you a map from memory. I know all the spots where the shore is rough and rocky. When a ship's company wants me to build a light-house, I know the best place to put it."

"I love the sea," Louis said. "I like to travel. Perhaps I shall be a lighthouse builder, after all."

"Certainly you will," his father said. "In the meantime, you must learn your arithmetic well. Someday you will spend hours over a drafting board. You will have to understand plans and blueprints."

Louis looked unhappy. The future did not sound at all interesting.

"Here's your supper, Master Lou," Cummy announced from the doorway.

She was carrying a small silver tray. On it was a bowl of steaming oatmeal. A lump of yellow butter was melting in its center. She placed the tray on a small table and drew up a chair for Louis.

Mr. Stevenson rose to go downstairs. "Eat plenty of that, laddie, and you will be sailing to the Hebrides (*hehb' ruh deez*) Islands with me before you know it. There's nothing like good Scotch porridge to fill out a bairn's ribs and make him strong and healthy."

He went out the door. Louis heard his firm tread on the stairs.

The boy did not eat his supper. Instead, he ran to the front window and pressed his nose against the pane.

"What do you see?" Cummy asked.

He did not answer her. His small body quivered with excitement.

"Here he comes!" he cried. "He has just turned the corner. I see a light! Now there are two lights!"

Each night an old lamplighter came to

15

light the street lamps which lined the sidewalk. He carried a short ladder and a long
torch. Each time he stood on the ladder to
touch the wick of the lamp above him, another light flared into the darkness.

Louis knew that the lamplighter would look up when he came to 17 Heriot Row. There was a lamp near the front door. The boy looked for his friend every night. He called him Leerie.

Now Leerie had arrived at the brightly lighted house. He placed the small ladder against the lamp post. Then he raised his head to see if Louis was standing by the window. The boy waved eagerly. The old man waved in return.

The lamplighter held out the arm which carried the torch. He was pretending to hand it to Louis. After that he climbed up the ladder and touched the flame to the wick of the lamp above. Another light glowed.

Louis gave a happy wriggle as he turned to Cummy. His dark eyes were dancing with happiness.

"I shan't be a lighthouse builder," he told her. "When I grow up, I shall go around with Leerie and light the lamps."

Escape at Bedtime

The lights from the parlor and kitchen shone out
    Through the blinds and the windows and bars;
And high overhead and all moving about,
    There were thousands of millions of stars.
There ne'er were such thousands of leaves on a tree,
    Nor of people in church or the Park,
As the crowds of the stars that looked down upon me,
    And that glittered and winked in the dark.

The Dog, and the Plow, and the Hunter, and all,
    And the star of the sailor, and Mars,
These shone in the sky, and the pail by the wall
    Would be half full of water and stars.
They saw me at last, and they chased me with cries,
    And they soon had me packed into bed;
But the glory kept shining and bright in my eyes,
    And the stars going round in my head.

A Child's Garden of Verses

CHAPTER 2

The Toy Theater

The two boys faced each other in the long drawing room of the Stevenson home. Louis, age seven, gazed at his cousin Bob, age nine, as though he feared he might disappear.

"I can't believe you are really going to stay all winter with us," Louis said happily.

"All winter!" the older boy answered. "Think of the fun we'll have!"

Louis nodded. Bob Stevenson was one of his favorite cousins. Not that cousins were anything new to him. He had about fifty, but most of them were Balfours on his mother's side of the family. Bob was Uncle Alan's boy, and Uncle Alan was Mr.

Stevenson's brother. Uncle Alan was an artist. He had refused to be an engineer.

What a cousin Bob was! He could think of wonderful games: pirates, robbers, highwaymen, wars. There was no end to his ideas.

The sound of voices drifted in from the big front hall. Before the boys could turn around, a gay voice spoke.

"Where's the birthday boy?"

"It's Aunt Jane!" Louis exclaimed.

A tall, sweet-looking woman entered the room. She was carrying a box wrapped in paper and ribbons. She handed it to Louis.

"Happy birthday, nephew — and may you have many happy returns of the day." She made a funny face at Bob. "Your turn will come later."

"Thank you, Auntie!" Louis exclaimed. "I had almost forgotten that it is my birthday."

"Aren't you going to open the box?" Bob asked him.

"Give me time!" Louis protested.

He set the box down on a chair and began to fumble with the ribbon. Bob whipped out a pocket knife and cut the knots. Without wasting a second, Louis tore off the paper.

"Oh!"

The joyful cry came from both boys. The present was a toy theater. The tiny stage was open at either end to let in wooden grooves which held cardboard actors. There were real curtains of crimson silk. They were cleverly operated by small cords. There were even make-believe footlights in front of the stage. The boys were delighted. Aunt Jane looked pleased.

"Just look here," Bob said.

Louis looked over his cousin's shoulder. The older boy was holding a sheet of colored figures — characters from *Aladdin and His Wonderful Lamp*.

"Here's Aladdin!" Louis exclaimed. "And his wicked uncle — and the Genie of the Lamp — and the Princess. I say, this is jolly!"

"You may get more plays at a stationer's

21

shop on Leith (*leeth*) Way," Aunt Jane said. "There are many to choose from."

Mother had just come into the room. "Here is a shilling to spend as you please, Lou," she said. "You may go to the shop right away if you like."

The boys ran out the door. They couldn't wait to reach the shop on Leith Way. They ran at a dogtrot most of the way.

A little bell tinkled overhead as they entered. The old shopkeeper came forward to meet them. Louis fingered the coin in his pocket.

"Please, sir . . ." he began. Then his eyes fell on the treasures on the counter. "Look, Bob! Here they are. Plays — dozens of them!"

The boys looked at the stack of booklets. There were many of them. *The Red Rover, The Blind Boy, The Old Oak Chest, The Wood Daemon, Jack Sheppard, The Smuggler, Richard I, Robin Hood, Three-Fingered Jack, The Terror of Jamaica,* and many others.

Louis's eyes were shining. "We will have a different play every night. Maybe two of them. I can buy several with my shilling."

"Look here, Lou. They are both plain and colored. The plain ones are a penny, and the colored ones are twopence. Let's buy the penny ones and save our money — that is, your money. Then we'll have the fun of painting our own actors. I'll paint them if you want me to. My father gave me a box of paints when I left home."

"I can paint and draw, too," Louis told him. "I drew pictures to illustrate 'The History of Moses.' Mother wrote the story down as I told it to her. I didn't win the prize Uncle David offered his nephews, but he gave me a special award. He said the Israelites with their tall hats and yellow trousers won him, whatever he meant by that."

"All right," Bob agreed. "We both will paint. Now, which plays shall we buy?"

Louis looked with longing at the books. He would have liked to buy them all.

"I suppose I must choose," he said at last. "Let's take *Robin Hood* and *The Red Rover*. And we must have *Three-Fingered Jack* and *The Terror of Jamaica*. Those last two sound blood-curdling."

The boys waited while the old man wrapped their purchase and made their change. When he handed the package across the counter, Louis took it eagerly. What fun Bob and he would have getting their play ready! They would show it to Mother and Aunt Jane. And he mustn't forget Cummy. She pretended to disapprove of the theater, but he didn't believe she really did. She could never read the Psalms in such a grand manner if she really disliked play-acting.

Outside the store the boys stood still for a minute. To the left lay the wharves and the white-sailed ships. Any other time the boys would have hurried down to the water's edge, but not today.

The package in Louis's hands seemed magic to him. "I'll race you home!" he cried.

They were off. Louis had a head start on

25

Bob, but Bob's legs were longer. Both boys fairly flew over the sandy stretch in the direction of Heriot Row.

Soon they were in sight of home. It was almost dark. Lights were beginning to shine out from the windows.

By now Louis was ten paces behind his older cousin. He caught for support at the iron railings of the little park that ran the length of the street.

Bob turned around. "Come on! Are you all right?"

Louis nodded. He was so short of breath that his head was swimming. The houses seemed to be turning around and around.

With a great effort he spurted across the cobblestones and caught up with Bob. The other boy had just opened the front door.

"It's a tie!" Louis gasped. "You didn't beat me after all. Now let's go in and give our play."

It was a quieter performance than the two cousins had planned. Although Louis was weary, he would not tell anyone. But he was glad to have Bob slide the cardboard actors on and off the toy stage. Bob read all the lines of *Robin Hood,* too. Louis, white-faced but smiling, sat by and listened. Bob took the different parts well. Louis was satisfied.

He sat by the fireside and said nothing. But in his heart he was with Robin Hood in Sherwood Forest. Up and down the glades he ran, escaping from the Sheriff of Nottinghamshire and attacking the wealthy Normans who had robbed the poor Saxons. When Robin Hood finally fired an arrow from the cardboard tower to mark his final resting place, Louis was half asleep in the chimney corner.

Cummy came bustling into the room. "Just look!" she complained. "My poor bairn is almost worn out. I'll carry him off to bed."

The poor bairn leaped up from his chair. His brown eyes were dancing. "I'm not tired, Cummy. I'll go to bed soon. I've something to do first. I must go outside for just a wee minute."

27

"You'll catch your death of cold, Master Lou," Cummy wailed. "Do throw a wrap about your shoulders."

He snatched the jacket from her as he passed. Only the sound of the banging door and Cummy's grim look told that Bob and he had been in the room.

Out on the front steps young Louis stared up into the night sky. The stars shone like jewels above him.

He pointed upward with a sweep of his thin little arm. "There's the North Star," he told Bob, who stood beside him. "They call it the sailors' star sometimes because ships steer by it. And there is Mars — that big red one. And that group is Orion the Hunter. Oh, Bob, aren't they beautiful?"

"What an odd one you are!" Bob said, laughing. "You never settle down, do you?"

"Who wants to settle down?" Louis answered.

"Master Lou!" Cummy's voice came from inside the house. "Please come in at once."

A man's deep voice boomed from inside

the house. "Smoutie! Come to bed. No more foolishness."

Louis shrugged his shoulders. "That's Father. When he says come to bed, I go to bed. But I know I'll never go to sleep. Pictures keep running through my head, pictures of Robin Hood and his merry men — Aladdin and his wonderful lamp — stories of my own about robbers and pirates and adventures — lonely ships away out on the ocean. And they expect me to go quietly to bed. I can't do it!"

CHAPTER 3

Visit to the Manse

"Here comes your grand-father," Cummy called up the stairs.

"Hurrah!" Louis cried.

It seemed to him that he had been waiting hours for those words. This was the day he was leaving Edinburgh (*ed' in bur oh*) for a week's visit with Grandfather and Aunt Jane in the big yellow house at Colinton, five miles away.

"Hurry, Lou," his mother called from the lower hall.

The young boy flew down the broad stairway. Through the open front door he could see the Reverend Doctor Balfour in his two-wheeled carriage behind the big bay horse.

31

The carriage was drawn up to the curb. Grandfather held the reins tightly. He was straight as an arrow, even though he was in his seventies. He looked grand in his tall silk hat and black coat.

The boy ran out the door and down the outside steps of the house to the sidewalk. In a hop, skip, and a jump, he was beside the carriage. Grandfather put out his hand and pulled Louis up beside him.

Cummy was close behind, carrying his traveling bag. She strapped it carefully behind the carriage.

Mrs. Stevenson came hurrying out. "Now, Lou, do be careful," she warned. "Don't play too hard. Tell Aunt Jane if your throat is sore. Father, you mustn't let him go out in the night air."

The old white-haired gentleman gave a snort. "Margaret, I have raised a houseful of children."

"But Lou is not strong," she protested.

Grandfather clucked to the horse. The carriage moved slowly down the street. Louis threw a farewell kiss to Mother and Cummy, who were still standing at the curb.

The boy stole a glance upward at his grandfather. Louis loved the old gentleman, but he feared him a little, too.

For a short time they rode along in silence. But Louis could never keep quiet. All sorts of ideas were bubbling in his mind. At last he could hold back no longer.

"I can hardly wait, Grandfather! The river and the mill and the swing under the elm tree on the west slope — are they still there?"

"They're still there," his grandfather said dryly. "Still there and not likely to leave. You will be the one to grow up and leave, Louis."

His grandson shook his head. "I shall never leave. I'd like to live at the manse the rest of my life — at least in the summertime. Who is there, Grandfather — Minnie, Willie, Henrietta?"

The old man nodded. "Those three and some other cousins, too. There were six or seven bairns playing about when I left. You know how your Aunt Jane is. She likes the place running over with boys and girls."

Louis bounced up and down. "I can hardly wait," he said again. He remembered the fun he had had with Bob the past winter. He felt lucky to have so many cousins.

After a while the carriage with its two passengers rolled into the little village of Colinton. Grandfather raised his hat several times to people on the street. Everyone knew the minister of the gray stone church.

In Scotland the minister's house is always called the manse. The manse at Colinton was a big yellow brick dwelling at the far end of the village. Here Louis's mother, her sister Jane, and their brothers had spent their childhood. Now the grandchildren came to visit in the old home each summer.

The carriage turned in at the manse gate. Soon it reached the house. Grandfather pulled at the reins. The bay horse came to a standstill. Boys and girls ran out of the house at the sound of wheels.

Louis jumped over the wheel and down on the ground. He was ready for action at once.

"Let's go down to the river and play pirates!" he shouted.

"Let's go!" the boys cried. "It's always more fun when you come, Lou."

"What about us?" Henrietta and Minnie demanded.

Louis looked at them. "You, too," he said. "There must have been girl pirates, wives and daughters or something-or-other."

The cousins started racing for the gently flowing stream at the foot of the hill. The little river was their favorite spot. Now that Louis had come, the best times of all would begin.

"Robert Louis Stevenson!" his grandfather called sternly.

Louis stopped short. He knew better than to disobey.

"Yes, sir?"

"Take your valise into the house. Greet your Aunt Jane."

The boy ran to the back of the carriage. His fingers worked at the leather strap that held his luggage in place. He turned toward his waiting cousins.

"Don't you dare leave without me," he warned. "I'll be right back."

He was off at a run toward the manse. Aunt Jane was waiting at the front door. Louis gave her a hug and a kiss. He rushed back to his playmates.

"I'll race you to the river!" he shouted.

The children dashed down the slope that led to the winding stream..

Aunt Jane, smiling, nodded to Grandfather. "Something is always happening wherever Lou is," she said.

Louis and the Balfour children had played hard all day. They had hardly stopped since breakfast. As usual, Louis had been their leader. He was commander of the troops, admiral of the fleet, chief of the pirates, and head explorer.

Now they were playing the old game "How Many Miles to Babylon?" Louis was very tired. He felt that he must be getting a fever again. His face was hot, and he ached all over.

"What a bother!" he muttered. "Aunt Jane will put me to bed if she finds out."

"Maybe she won't find out," a voice whispered at his ear.

Louis gave a start. His little cousin Minnie from India was gazing at him with her big brown eyes. She slipped a cool hand into his.

"Why don't you rest for a while?" she suggested. "Maybe you will be all right by supper time."

"Will you come with me?" he begged. "I hate to go off alone."

The two stole quietly away from the other children. They crept into the cool, darkened house and up the wide front stairs. They tiptoed down the upper hall and peeped into Grandfather's bedroom. The great walnut bed looked huge enough for a giant.

"It always makes me think of the three bears," Minnie said with a giggle. "Goldilocks lay down on the Big Bear's bed, but it was too hard."

Louis seized her idea at once. "Then she tried the middle-sized bed, but it was too soft. Aunt Jane must be the Middle-Sized Bear."

By now the children were in the little bedroom with the sloping eaves which Louis
claimed as his own. Years ago it had belonged to his mother.

The exhausted boy threw himself across
the bed and closed his eyes.

"Are you asleep?" Minnie whispered.

"No, I'm just resting," Louis answered.
His eyes were still closed.

Minnie sat down on a low chair beside
his bed. "I'm sorry you are tired, but I think
this is jolly. It makes me think of India,
where everyone comes in out of the heat in
the afternoon."

"Would you rather live in India or Scotland?" Louis asked.

The little girl's eyes opened wide in surprise. "How can you even ask? India, of
course. I love to visit Grandfather and Aunt
Jane and see all my cousins, but I shall be
glad to go back to India when the boat sails.
India is the most wonderful place in the
whole world."

Louis sat up in bed. "Tell me about it."

Minnie gave him a gentle push. "I will — if you promise to rest."

He lay back and closed his eyes again. " Go ahead."

"India is a very different country from Scotland," Minnie began. "It's like a land in a storybook. There are crowds of people everywhere. Nearly every day there are parades in the city where I live. The flutes play, the drums beat, and the people chant. And down in the market place the merchants have all sorts of food for sale — but my ayah (*ah' ya*) seldom allows me to buy any."

"*Ayah?*" Lou tried out the word.

Minnie nodded. "My nurse."

A smile broke over Louis's face. "Oh, yes. Like Cummy. She is my *ayah*."

"*You* might think India is a smelly place," Minnie went on. "But I love it. There's something to see every minute. There may be a snake charmer on one street corner, a fakir (*fah keer'*) — an Indian magician — on another corner, and a priest with his begging bowl on still another."

41

"I would like to go to India — or any far-away country," Louis declared.

He was sitting straight up in bed now. His eyes were gazing into the distance.

"You may go to India right now," she told him.

"How?"

"You know that black teakwood cabinet at the end of the hall downstairs?"

Louis nodded.

"It came from India. It is filled with things from India. I can tell you about most of them. It would be almost like a trip to India. I hope no one catches us. We children aren't supposed to open the cabinet. But, after all, my mother and father sent it here."

The two cousins tiptoed hand in hand down the stairs to the long hall. There was not a sound anywhere. Louis's dark eyes traveled from the teakwood cabinet to his Cousin Minnie's face. Here was someone who had really walked on other shores and seen people of another race.

"There's a pair of elephant tusks," she

42

said, pointing to two curved pieces of ivory. "And there's a bell such as elephants wear around their necks. There are bells of every size and kind in India. Where I live, we hear the temple bells many times each day."

Louis opened one of the glass doors. It gave a little creak. He daringly lifted out the elephant's bell. It gave forth a deep musical note. The children jumped. They glanced about. Suppose someone had heard it. Suppose they were discovered. But there was only silence in the big house.

Outside from the wide lawn the sounds of voices drifted in through the front door:

> How far is it to Babylon?
> Three-score miles and ten!

Louis and Minnie explored the cabinet further. The little girl pointed to a stuffed bird with brightly colored plumage.

"It's a mynah bird," she said.

But Louis did not hear her. He was examining a richly embroidered headdress. "Who wears this?"

43

"A Hindu girl," Minnie told him. "She wears it only on special days. A Hindu girl's festival clothes are like something out of a fairy tale."

Louis gave an excited wriggle. "I have an idea, Minnie. When we grow up, I'll marry you. Then we can go to India together."

"But I'm going back next month," Minnie reminded him.

"That's all right. You can come to Scotland again. I'll wait for you," Louis told her kindly. "I simply must get to India. I want to travel all over the world."

Again the children's voices rose from the lawn:

> Can I get there by candlelight?
> Yes, and back again.

He caught her hand. "Come along. I've rested long enough. I feel much better. Let's go and see what the others are doing. I don't want to miss a single thing."

CHAPTER 4

Trouble at School

There was a new pupil at the Edinburgh Academy. Ten-year-old Louis Stevenson had entered its doors for the first time this morning.

"I don't know where to put him," the assistant headmaster said unhappily. "He can't spell. He can't do sums. He knows nothing about Latin."

"That's strange," the headmaster said. "He knows as much history as a boy in the Upper Form. He recited Sir Walter Scott's *Marmion* to me until I had to stop him."

Louis sat quietly by. He looked from one man's face to the other's. It seemed to him that they were doing a great deal of foolish talking. After all, why should he study what he did not want to study?

"Let him sit with the younger boys," the headmaster said firmly. "He must learn that a boy must do his tasks well if he expects to go up with his classmates."

So for several hours Louis had sat in a roomful of small boys. He was at least a head taller than they were. But they did their sums easily, while he labored over a paper that grew dirtier and dirtier.

At last the master stood up behind his desk and tapped a little bell. He looked down from his platform at the class.

"You may go out to play," he told them.

The boys filed out the door. Louis started to follow them when he felt a hand on his shoulder.

"I want to talk with you, young Stevenson," the master said.

Louis was uncomfortable. He had felt very awkward among the little boys. Now he felt equally awkward as his eyes met those of the master.

"You don't seem stupid," the man said in a kind voice. "You must work hard and try to

48

catch up with the other boys your own age."

Louis did not answer. He felt angry. The man seemed to think he actually *was* a little stupid.

"Speak up," the master commanded. "Don't just stand there."

"I can learn when I want to, sir," the boy answered. "It's just that I don't care for some subjects. I don't see any use in them. But I love literature and history."

The master frowned. "You don't have the proper attitude. You cannot study just the subjects you like. Now, along with you. Go out and get some fresh air. Roll and tumble with the rest of the boys."

Louis walked slowly out to the playground. At first it seemed deserted. Then he turned a corner of the building and came upon a ring of boys. Two lads in the center were sparring with each other with all their might. Just as he came up, one of them dealt the other a mighty blow. The boy dropped with a thud to the ground.

"One, two, three, four, five . . ."

49

"He's down for good!" a voice shouted.

". . . six, seven, eight, nine, ten!"

"Edwin is the winner!" the boys yelled.

The loser picked himself up, walked a few shaky steps, and put out his hand to the boy named Edwin. The crowd cheered wildly.

The referee turned to Louis. "You're next," he announced. "We always let new boys prove themselves this way."

Louis's mouth flew open. He gazed in horror at the scene. He felt sick. The winner was jumping about the ring. The loser was mopping away at a bloody nose. All eyes were upon Louis.

He shook his head. "No, thanks. I've never fought in my life. Maybe I'll learn someday, but I doubt it. I just don't believe I'd like it."

They all stared at him. They could not believe that he was refusing. Louis stared back at them. All his life he had been sheltered and protected because he was not strong.

"Coward!" someone called from the circle.

Tears of rage sprang to Louis's eyes. He doubled up his fists and stepped forward. The boy who faced the group was not afraid.

"I'm not a coward!" he said. "It's not my fault that I've been sick. I may not be able to fight you, but I can swim, fish, canoe, and ride horseback as well as any of you. And I wish I were strong enough to pound your heads into a pulp!"

51

They fell back before his fury. At that moment the school bell rang. One by one, they filed silently back through the tall gray columns into the stone building.

Louis walked alone with his head held high. They had made no bruises on his body, but they had hurt his pride.

☆ ☆ ☆

One day after Louis had been attending the Academy for two years, his father said, "How would you like to forget school for a while and cross the Channel to France?"

Louis looked down at his dog, Coolin. "What would we do with him?"

"Your Uncle David will keep him for us. He will be well taken care of. I intend to go to France."

Louis's dark eyes danced. "You really mean it?"

"I really mean it. Your mother has been far from well this winter. You have had your usual share of coughs and colds. I need a vacation from my work. We shall go to Nice (*nees*) in the south of France. We shall stay there until April or even later."

Mrs. Stevenson had come into the room. She coughed slightly and drew her soft wool shawl closer about her shoulders.

"Do you think Lou will miss too much school?" she asked anxiously. "I suppose I must go, since the doctor has ordered me to. But Lou could stay here with Cummy. She would take good care of him."

Lou waited breathlessly for his father's answer.

"Nonsense!" Thomas Stevenson replied. "I would rather have him a cheerful idiot than a sickly genius."

Louis turned a handspring in the middle of the room. "Hurrah!" he cried. He came to an upright position and grinned at his father. "Maybe I can be a cheerful genius."

Mr. Stevenson looked at him lovingly. "You are a terrible nuisance. Now go and help Cummy decide what to pack for you. We shall be leaving in a few days."

CHAPTER 5

Off to France

Early one morning soon after Christmas, Louis and his family set out for London. From there they took the boat train to Dover and went aboard the Channel boat.

The crossing was rough. Mrs. Stevenson stayed below the entire way, and Cummy remained with her.

Mr. Stevenson walked up and down the deck. He seemed to enjoy the wind, rain, and dashing waves. Louis, who adored his father, tried to stay with him. However, the rolling of the boat was too much for him. The boy had to flee to calmer quarters.

Soon they were in Paris. To Louis, the city was a wonderland, even in January. The

Stevensons stayed at a comfortable inn, but every night Father took them to dine at a different hotel.

Louis's great dark eyes drank in the beauty of the sparkling lights. He watched the little groups of well-dressed people at the tables. He saw the eager waiters in their black coats hurrying about. He enjoyed the strange new dishes and the old ones served in French style. While he did not say so, he thought Parisian cooking better than Scotch.

Every afternoon Father hired a carriage and took them about the city. As the boy rode down the Champs Élysées (*shawn zay lee zay'*), he looked at the horse chestnut trees bordering the avenue and wondered how they looked in springtime when they were in bloom.

When they had arrived in Paris, Louis had known only a few words of schoolboy French. Now he began to pick up the language with ease. He liked this great city where people took the time to be polite and thoughtful. Such familiar phrases as *Pardon, Madame* and

Merci, Monsieur fell so often upon his ears that he began to use them and other French terms without even thinking.

"I like Paris," he told his father. "I think I would like to be a Frenchman."

Mr. Stevenson raised his eyebrows. "You would? How about Edinburgh — and Castle Hill with the soldiers marching and the bugles playing? Do they mean nothing to you?"

A wave of homesickness swept over Louis at his father's words. Gone was Paris with its broad avenues. Gone was the musical speech of its people. For a moment Louis saw his bleak, windy native city and heard the Scottish accents of his countrymen.

"Auld Reekie!" he whispered.

That was the name given Edinburgh by Scotchmen all over the world. It was the name that came to Louis now as he thought of his birthplace.

His homesickness passed as quickly as it had come. But his eyes were tender when he spoke.

"You are right, Father. There is no place like Edinburgh, but I am enjoying Paris very, very much."

Before long the Stevensons traveled down to the south of France. Long before they arrived at their stopping place, they could feel the warm breezes of a milder climate. The sun shone all day. There was hardly a cloud in the sky.

Louis glanced up at his father. "The sky is as blue as my father's eyes," he thought.

In Nice they stayed at a hotel for six weeks. Then they moved on to Menton (*mahn tohn'*), where they took a furnished house. Here a confectioner sent in their evening meal. Cummy, with the help of a little French girl, prepared breakfast and lunch.

"I'm glad we made the change," Louis said happily. "There were so many times you did not feel like coming down to the dining room, Mother, and now we are all together again. It was lonely, eating by myself when Father was upstairs with you."

Louis had private school lessons in the

morning. The rest of the day was his to do with as he pleased.

One day he fished with a rod and a line from an old stone bridge in the shallow waters around Menton. The day was warm. The fish were biting. In a few hours his catch numbered thirty.

He turned his head once by chance. The fish were flopping on the stones. Some of them were already still. Their misery clutched at his heart.

"Pshaw!" he muttered.

With one move he swept them all back into the blue waters beneath him. In another moment he was on his way back to the house. He could not enjoy a sport that hurt other creatures.

Gradually the warm air and the healing sunlight did wonders for his hacking cough. Mrs. Stevenson, too, made a steady improvement. Meanwhile, Louis roamed the town and the countryside. He went down to the seashore every day to watch the fishermen haul in their nets.

He made friends with a shepherd boy and sat with him on a hillside while the sheep nibbled on the slope below. At sundown he helped him count the sheep.

"Un, deux, trois, quatre, cinq . . ." Louis counted.

"Six, sept, huit, neuf, dix." the shepherd finished. "You speak like a Frenchman, *mon ami.*"

Louis flushed with pleasure. He was eager to speak like a native. He knew now that he must be succeeding.

Finally he began to tire of his visit. More and more he thought of the empty house at 17 Heriot Row. The part of Edinburgh

that he loved best — the crooked streets and shabby buildings of Old Town — kept coming to his mind. And Coolin! Coolin was the best dog a boy ever had. How was he getting along? Did he miss his master?

One morning at the breakfast table Thomas Stevenson looked at his family. He rubbed his hands together with satisfaction.

"You both look healthy and rosy as Scottish people should look," he told his wife and son. "The change of climate has been good for all of us. We start for home tomorrow."

In the next room Cummy gave a sigh of relief. "Now I shall have a decent cup of tea," she said to herself. "These Frenchmen don't know what proper tea is."

But Louis was not thinking of tea. Coolin's small black furry face came before his eyes. "I shall soon see Coolin!" he exclaimed. "Oh, Father, you don't think Coolin has forgotten me, do you?"

"Of course not," Mr. Stevenson assured him. "Coolin is far too sensible a dog for that."

61

Great is the sun, and wide he goes
Through empty heaven without repose;
And in the blue and glowing days
More thick than rain he showers his rays.

from "Summer Sun"

CHAPTER 6

The Lantern Bearers

It was summer. The Stevensons had been at North Berwick on the Scottish seacoast for over a month. Since Grandfather Balfour had died, the old house at Colinton was no longer the gathering place for the clan. Aunt Jane had moved away. There were new faces in the manse.

At first Louis had been very unhappy about it all.

"Life must go on," Mother told him. "The manse belongs to other people now."

"I wish I were still there," the boy said sadly.

Now the Stevensons spent the summer vacations at the seashore. They had tried several places, but North Berwick was their favorite. It was a little fishing village that stretched into the sea not many miles from Edinburgh.

Of course, Cummy was with them. She was almost like a member of the family. Coolin also had been allowed to come. The black Skye terrier was a two-man dog. He followed both Mr. Stevenson and Louis. But when the father and the son separated, he usually trotted on his short little legs after the boy.

Louis was thirteen years old. He felt completely at home in North Berwick. Many other families from Edinburgh came to the little village during the summer months. Several of the Balfour cousins were usually there at the same time as the Stevensons.

Nearly every day Louis went swimming or sailing with his father. The young boy enjoyed these times when his father was not too busy to be with him. In the city Mr. Stevenson went to his office directly after breakfast and remained there until dark. In his own mind, his son thought this was a great waste of time when the world was so full of more interesting things than drafting boards and figures.

Louis had a number of playmates at North Berwick who were his own age. Tonight they had planned their favorite pastime. He was hurrying through his supper so that he might join them. He felt a warm glow as he thought of what lay ahead.

"You have hardly touched your haddock," his mother said, interrupting his thoughts. Louis wrinkled up his nose.

"You must eat everything on your plate," his father told him.

The boy sighed. He wanted to please his parents, but sometimes it seemed to him that they were never satisfied.

"When you have finished eating, we will go into the parlor," Mr. Stevenson said. "I have planned to read aloud to you."

Louis almost cried aloud. Sky and sea and high adventure were waiting just beyond the four walls, and his father intended to imprison him.

"Oh, no, Father!" he exclaimed. "I promised the boys that I'd meet them after supper.

Thomas Stevenson frowned. The evening was not going as he had planned it. All day he had thought of sitting by an early autumn fire with his wife and son.

Louis's mother glanced nervously from her husband to their son. These two whom she loved most seemed to disagree all too often.

She gave Mr. Stevenson a pleading look. "We will soon be back in the city. Then we shall have many evenings together. Perhaps we should allow Louis to go out tonight."

A short time later the boy fled out of the house into the darkness. He was grateful to his mother for her part in his escape. But the memory of his father's disappointed face rose before him. He ran on. There was no time to think of that now.

As he ran, he hugged his special treasure to the front of his leather coat. It was a tin ship's lantern, the kind sold in every small shop along the fishing coast. It was a common household article for those who went down to the sea in ships. But for Louis it had a special meaning.

In the shelter of a wall the boy stopped and struck a match. He sheltered the little flame

carefully from the night breeze. Then he touched the match to the wick. He turned it so that it would not smoke. His nervous fingers pulled the tin slide over the lantern's opening. He hugged the lantern with one arm as he ran.

He could feel the warmth of the lantern at his waist. Not a ray of light showed from the hidden flame. Anyone meeting him would never have dreamed that he carried the token of a secret band.

The main street of the little village was almost deserted. The fall nights were chilly. Most people were at home behind closed doors. As Louis hurried along, he could hear sounds of laughter and singing from the town inn. From the cobbler's shop next door there came the *tap-tap-tap* of a hammer. The old man was working late tonight.

Suddenly in the shadow of a low dwelling Louis came face to face with another boy. "Do you have your lantern?" Louis whispered.

"Yes," the boy answered.

"Good. Let us go on and find the others."

They set off at a dogtrot. They did not speak again until they were on the outskirts of the town. The houses became fewer and fewer. At last a third boy joined them.

"Do you have your lantern?" Louis asked.

The newcomer nodded. The three went on their way. Before long the twinkling lights of the village lay behind them. In front of them lay a sandy stretch of beach. The night was inky black, but the *boom-boom-boom* of the waves came to the boys' ears.

Ahead of them they could barely see the outlines of an abandoned fishing boat. It was a huge craft which had been manned in its day by thirty or forty men. This boat was the boys' goal.

As they approached the hulk, a dark form rose up from the shadows. "Who goes there?" he demanded in a low voice.

"The Red Rover and his men," Louis answered in a dramatic whisper.

The challenger turned his head toward the boat. "Stevenson and his friends," he announced to his unseen companions on the boat.

"Let them pass!" a voice from inside the boat commanded.

Louis and the boys scrambled over the side of the wreck. Helping hands reached out to pull them up. Presently a half-dozen eager young faces shone in the glow of as many ship's lanterns which by now were opened. The pounding of the surf only a few yards away lent an air of mystery to the scene.

"You are late," one of the boys said to young Stevenson.

Louis shrugged his shoulders good-naturedly. "I had to eat my fish before I came."

"Eat your fish!"

The speaker's voice was a mixture of horror and amusement.

Louis rolled his eyes. He could not resist this chance to be the center of the stage. "Every bite of it. And my father saw that I drank my milk and ate my scone, too."

"Zounds!" one of his hearers gasped. "What we must put up with!"

"I came as soon as I could," Louis assured him. "I'll pay with a ghost story for my tardiness."

"Not a ghost story," another listener objected. "I'd rather hear the one about the ship that pirates plundered near this very spot."

"No," a second boy said. "Tell about the man hidden under the floor in the deserted castle."

"Just get started," a third member pleaded. "Remember, we can't stay here all night."

A pale moon had risen over the horizon. Its silver rays shone down upon the boys huddled in the bow of the old boat.

Louis was their leader. His eyes sparkled as he spun his tale for his listeners. His words wove a magic spell over them.

". . . and from the cellar of the great castle there came an unearthly moan," he related.

The boys listened openmouthed. The moments passed. The moon rose higher in the sky. At last the storyteller brought his narrative to an end. The night was still.

71

"It's growing late," he said, running his thin fingers through his long hair. "That will be enough for tonight. Darken your lanterns, men. We will leave in pairs. You will be notified of the next meeting. Until then — farewell."

He leaped over the side of the boat and down on the sand. A companion came close behind him. Together they made their way back toward the village. In a few minutes two more boys left the boat. Finally the last ones left. The meeting of the Lantern Bearers was over for another time.

CHAPTER 7

"I'll Never Be an Engineer!"

I have rented a cottage at Swanston," Mr. Stevenson told his wife and son over the breakfast table.

Louis's eyes shone. He was nearly seventeen. In the autumn he would enter Edinburgh University. "Do you hear that, Coolin?" he said to the Skye terrier stretched out at his feet. "Soon you will be a country dog. How will you like that?"

Coolin opened one eye and shut it again. He was an old dog now. There were many white hairs in his stiff, bristly coat. Louis could hardly remember the time when Coolin had not been a part of the family.

"It will be almost like living at Colinton,"

Mrs. Stevenson said. "Swanston is only a few miles from the manse."

Mr. Stevenson nodded. "It's a bonny spot in the Pentland Hills. Those hills keep away the cold, damp east winds. As a girl at Colinton, you were well and strong. I have a feeling that the air of Swanston will agree with you and Lou."

"I for one shall be glad to stay in Scotland," Louis said.

His father smiled. "I think Swanston may be just what we are looking for."

The Stevensons went to their new summer home in May. From the beginning Louis was enchanted by the rambling stone cottage nestled in the Pentland Hills.

There was no one his own age for several miles, but he did not care greatly. He had no close friends in Edinburgh. He wished sometimes for his cousin Bob, but Bob and his family had moved to France. Bob had liked books, walking, and talking, and these were Louis's chief interests. He walked alone much of the time.

The boy shivered whenever he remembered that his father expected him to become a lighthouse engineer.

"I'll never be an engineer!" he declared to Cummy.

"But what will you do, Master Lou, if you don't follow in your father's footsteps?" Cummy asked in despair.

She was still with the family. Now that Louis was almost a man, she stayed on as companion and maid to his mother.

"I don't know — but I'll not be an engineer," Louis declared with his jaw set.

"Don't tell your father," Cummy begged. "It will only make him angry. Your poor mother will take to her bed again if you two quarrel."

"I don't want to quarrel with him!" Louis exclaimed. "I love him more than anyone else in the world. Why can't he understand that I hate even the thought of being an engineer?"

There was much that Thomas Stevenson did not understand about his only son. He did not understand why the boy always went about with a notebook in his pocket. He did not understand how he could spend long hours writing stories and poems. He thought it a great waste of time on the young man's part. He thought Louis could have spent it better learning to be a lighthouse engineer.

Louis knew better than to try to explain it to him. He realized only too well that his father could be kinder than anyone he had ever known. But he could be stubborn, too. At times he seemed as hard as the Castle Rock that had watched over Edinburgh for centuries.

For several years Louis had wandered alone about the city whenever he could steal away from home. He was never happier than when he slipped into a shabby old velveteen jacket (of which his parents disapproved) and roamed about the Old Town. The people there seemed kinder and friendlier than those he met every day. He seemed to be looking for something.

"I feel smothered at home," he said to himself. "We have breakfast at the same time in the morning, and we dine at the same time in the evening. My mother entertains her friends one afternoon a week. On another afternoon she rides out in her carriage to make calls. Sometimes I have to go with her, and I'd rather take a beating. Sundays are worst of all. Reading aloud after dinner. Ugh!"

The boy escaped whenever he could. Down in the slum district where he felt happy and free, they called him Velvet Coat. They could not know that the slender, slightly homely youth with the beautiful, dark, flashing eyes was storing up sights and sounds and colors for books which the whole world would one day love.

On the whole, Louis was glad to go to Swanston. There, at least, his parents could not complain about the company he kept, for there would be none. And Coolin would have room to stretch his short legs and run.

It was Coolin who led his master into new

adventures. The little dog was constantly in trouble. One day he made away with a whole goose. That theft was scarcely over when he stole a leg of mutton. The cook threatened to beat him with her broom if he came near her kitchen again.

Louis thought it was funny, but he dared not show it. On the day of the thefts he took Coolin and set out for a long walk in the hills. He thought he had better leave with his pet until the cook's anger died down.

Coolin wandered in and out of the shrubs.

Now and then he ran back to his master as though he wished to tell him what lay ahead.

Louis was busy with his own thoughts. He paid little attention to the dog. He did not even notice when Coolin spied a flock of sheep on a hillside.

Suddenly the boy became aware of a great disturbance. The sheep ran and bleated madly. They scattered in all directions as though a demon were at their heels. But it was only Coolin in high spirits.

"Get thy dog away from my sheep!" a cross

old voice shouted from somewhere nearby.

"Coolin, Coolin! Come here!" Louis cried.

But he called in vain. It was too late. Confusion was everywhere. The old shepherd in his homespun smock was furious. His face was red with rage. He pounded on the ground with his long stick.

"Away with thee! Begone, and take thy dog!" he exclaimed.

Louis chased after Coolin. The dog ran like the wind. The pursuit only increased the noise and hubbub. But at last the boy ran the little beast down and caught him up in his arms.

"I'm sorry," Louis told the shepherd. "He's just a silly little old dog. He doesn't know any better."

The old man looked at the downcast face of the boy before him. "No matter," he said in a low voice. "There's little harm done."

"That's very kind of you," Louis told him.

He walked along beside the guardian of the sheep. The old man with the aid of his sheep dog had gathered his flock together. He glanced at Louis now and then.

"May I come along with you?" Louis asked.

The old man nodded. They walked a long distance in silence. The sun was very warm. A lark twittered in the distance. Louis felt peaceful and happy. Neither he nor the old man spoke for a time.

The old man was the first to break the silence. "These very stones would talk if they could." He stole a glance at Louis. "But thee probably does not know much Scottish history."

Louis laughed. "I have known the stories of the people who lived near here for a long time. My old nurse told me many stories about Scotland. No doubt you could tell me more — but I already know a good deal."

The old shepherd tapped Coolin gently with his crook. "He is not a bad doggy," he said gruffly.

That was his way of telling Louis that he accepted him and his mischievous pet.

The boy spent the rest of the afternoon
with his new friend. It was the beginning
of happy times that neither would ever forget. The old shepherd, John Todd, taught
Louis to love the hills about Swanston. The
boy, the man, and the dog Coolin became
fast friends. Indeed, Coolin found his last
resting place among the Swanston hills.
Several years later Louis wrote in Latin on a

wooden panel which was placed on the dog's grave:

> To Coolin, the gentle and friendly, who in a green old age, by some unhappy chance, met with his death at the place where three roads meet, where the hunters are wont to gather. This stone has been set up to his memory by his sorrowing friends. 1869, R.L.S.

But before that day came, the first summer at Swanston had ended, and Louis had become a student at Edinburgh University.

CHAPTER 8

An Underwater Adventure

September came much too soon. Louis left the freedom of the country and returned to the city, where he enrolled at the University. He attended engineering classes in mathematics and physics and hated them both.

Whenever he could escape from his duties, he donned the old velveteen jacket and roamed the poorer quarters of the city. There was usually a book in his hand or his pocket.

During the first summer after Louis started at the University, Mr. Stevenson sent him with work crews from place to place along the seacoast. He thought that experience with the crews during his vacation months would do the lad good. The older man was sure that his son would learn about the business of building lighthouses.

This was the year of the adventure at Wick. Here a crew of Mr. Stevenson's men were building a breakwater to protect shipping. Louis worked hard with them during the day. He measured distances with a steel line. He bent over a drafting board till his eyes were blurred.

But the nights were his own. He wrote page after page of stories and poems at a furious speed. Often he worked until dawn. These were the hours when he really lived. The work he did for his father seemed like a bad dream.

But one workaday event stood out in his memory. Time after time he had watched a daredevil named Bob Bain go down into the depths of the sea. At last Louis could keep still no longer.

"Bob, I want to borrow your diver's suit," he said.

Bob shook his head. "No. Your father wouldn't like it."

Louis persisted. "I *must* go down. Please lend me your suit. That's a good fellow."

At last the other yielded. Louis took the equipment eagerly and prepared to put it on.

Twenty pounds of lead were fastened to each of his feet. Then he was wrapped in woolen clothing until he looked like a huge cocoon. Finally his fellow workers set an awkward diver's helmet on his head.

The young Scot climbed slowly down the ladder into the calm, blue-green water. Before he stepped off the ladder, he felt for the rope and the rubber tube that meant safety.

A moment more and he was going down, down, down into the cold, deep water. Fish and other strange creatures of the deep swam past him. He reached out to touch

them. His hands moved slowly under the weight of the water, and the fish escaped him. He felt a strange peacefulness. He could not hear a sound in the silent depths.

All too soon he was forced to return to the world above. Each day brought the same boring tasks. The hours he could spare from sleep at night were not long enough to record the million and one ideas he had. He longed to escape the daytime drudgery, but he was imprisoned by his job.

The opening of his second year at college was a little better. He joined a debating society known as the Speculative Society, or "Spec." And his cousin Bob came home. Louis's heart lifted, for where Bob was, there were sure to be gaiety, nonsense, and laughter.

Mr. Stevenson had never cared greatly for Bob. He liked him even less now. He didn't like his views on life and religion. And he didn't like to have Bob around Louis, who was younger by two years.

Twelve months passed. That summer,

Louis went with his father on a voyage among the Hebrides Islands. The young man saw the poetry of the wild, rugged coast. His father saw only the need for lighthouses. The two were miles apart in their thinking.

It was during his third year at the University that Louis found the courage to tell his father that he had made up his mind to give up the study of engineering.

As usual, the Stevensons were at Swanston for the summer. Louis was out for a stroll with the tall, broad shouldered man he loved so dearly and feared so much.

He glanced nervously at his father several times. He wondered how he could bring himself to break the news.

Finally he took a headlong plunge. "Father, I have decided not to become an engineer."

Thomas Stevenson stopped short. "Will you repeat that statement?"

Louis's face was crimson. "I have decided not to become an engineer."

"Nonsense!" Mr. Stevenson barked. "Your grandfather was an engineer, my brother David and I are engineers, and you will be one, too."

Louis shook his head. "I intend to be a writer."

His father gave a short, bitter laugh. "A writer! You must be losing your mind."

"I have wanted to be a writer all my life," Louis went on. "I am never really happy except when I have a pen in my hand. Please try to understand how I feel, Father."

Mr. Stevenson walked ahead down the gravel path. He was fairly trembling with rage. Louis could hardly keep up with him. "I will not have it," the elder Stevenson was muttering. "I refuse to listen."

The son looked at his father's face and felt guilty at the unhappiness he saw there.

"Perhaps I could do something else," Louis said hopefully. "Perhaps I could read law."

Thomas Stevenson stopped again and looked hard at his son. Fortunately he could not read Louis's mind. The young man was thinking that a lawyer should have plenty of time to write after office hours.

His father's voice broke into his thoughts. "So you are considering the study of law. Now *that* I can accept."

In such a simple manner, Louis changed his career.

After that day Louis and his father seemed to understand each other. Mr. Stevenson still looked coldly at Bob whenever he came to visit. The young man's visits became further and further apart. This hurt Louis, for Bob was his hero. The two cousins met often outside the Stevenson home.

Meanwhile Louis found new friends at the Simpson house. Walter Simpson had been a childhood acquaintance and was now a fellow law student. With his brother Willie and his sister Eve, he welcomed Louis to their house across the park on Queen Street.

There were no older people, for their parents were dead. Their father had been the famous Doctor Simpson who had discovered chloroform. The young people lived alone in the house where they had grown up. Louis loved the free and easy atmosphere of their home. He was their favorite guest and a special pet of the old butler, Jarvis.

"He has a hungry look," the old man confided to Eve. "It hurts me to see him so thin and half-starved."

"I am sure the Stevensons set as good a table as ours, Jarvis," Eve Simpson replied. "Maybe he's just naturally thin. He seems happy enough — at least, when he's with us."

The old man shook his head. The tall, thin youth with the twinkling eyes puzzled him.

Once on Eve's birthday, her brothers and Louis dismissed the servants for the evening and prepared to serve the dinner party themselves. The brothers took over the kitchen. Louis acted as butler. For once he wore evening clothes instead of the velveteen jacket. He had decorated a couple of round Dutch cheeses with celery and garnishes so that they looked like human heads. Now they grinned down from the sideboard on the people seated about the table.

The guests laughed until tears rolled down their cheeks at the new butler's antics. Louis pranced to and fro with a napkin over his arm. He talked so much that his audi-

ence complained that the food was cold before he served it. The dinner was a huge success. It was far removed from the dull, formal ones at 17 Heriot Row.

In the summer of 1872, Louis went to Germany with Walter Simpson. It was a time to remember. The two youths sat in outdoor cafes and talked by the hour. Louis had discovered the American poet, Walt Whitman, and he was eager to share him with his friend.

The two young Scots had a wonderful time. They came home for the opening of the University. Another year passed. Now Louis was twenty-three. That summer he went on a walking tour to Suffolk County.

There he met a young widow, the lovely Fanny Sitwell, to whom he promptly lost his heart. She was eight years older than he, but she seemed to understand him as no one had ever understood him before. To her he poured out his inmost thoughts.

"I *must* write," he told her earnestly. "I cannot live without writing."

"Then write," Mrs. Sitwell said. "Do what you want to do, Louis, but really labor at it. Writing is work, and you must treat it like work."

Through her he met Sidney Colvin, a Cambridge art professor well known by London editors. These two people opened up for him a whole new world. Before he left for home, they had inspired him to write an essay on roads and to begin one on Walt Whitman.

But back in Edinburgh a storm was brewing. When Louis reached home, his father was waiting. He accused Louis of holding different beliefs from his. He did not realize that youth and age seldom think alike. Instead, he blamed Bob. He said that Bob should never come again to 17 Heriot Row. Louis was sick at heart. He became ill in body as well. A London doctor said he must have a change of scenery. He ordered him to go south — without his parents — for a long rest.

CHAPTER 9

"Pirates, Is It?"

Louis stayed in Menton, in the south of France, for five months. He came home healthier and happier. He had completed the essay on Walt Whitman and begun another called *Ordered South*. It was about his stay in Menton. And he had grown a mustache! All in all, his trip had been a success.

Somehow, after his return, things were easier between his father and him. Being apart had done them both good. Perhaps the elder Stevenson realized that the boy had grown into a man. He increased his allowance, which had been very small.

When winter came, Louis studied law once more. But his real interest lay in his writing. That was his first love, and it would be his last. His new friend, Sidney Colvin, introduced him to Leslie Stephen, the editor of the *Cornhill* magazine. His new acquaintance encouraged him to write.

Indeed, when Stephen came to Edinburgh in February of 1875 to lecture on mountain-climbing, he thought enough of Louis to look him up.

"I want you to make a visit with me," he told the young Scot. "There's a fellow in the Edinburgh Infirmary I'd like you to meet. I think the world will hear from him someday. He has sent me some poems worth reading."

"What is his name?" Louis asked.

"William Ernest Henley," Stephen replied.

The day for the visit had arrived. Louis followed the editor from London down the hall of the hospital. He was not prepared for the sight which greeted him upon his arrival in the ward. Louis had half-expected to find a pale, dreamy-eyed youth with a pad of paper in his hand and a book of poems at his elbow. Instead he saw a laughing giant of a man with a yellow beard. He lay in a bed between two small boys in cots on either side.

"Well, shiver my timbers, if it isn't Mr. Stephen," the giant's deep voice rumbled. "I though you were far away in the London fogs."

The editor of the *Cornhill* pulled out a chair for Louis and took another himself.

"On the contrary, I'm braving the Edinburgh mists to introduce two bra' Scotch writers. This is Louis Stevenson, Henley — although he signs his work Robert Louis Stevenson."

"I'd rather be called just Louis," the other visitor told the man in the bed.

Louis and the yellow-bearded giant regarded each other with interest. At last Henley spoke.

"He looks like a pirate to me. That long, thin face and those dancing eyes need only gold circles in his ears and a black patch over one eye to make him one."

Something in Louis warmed to the speaker's manner. "Pirates, is it?" he said softly. "Sir, you should see the spot on the seacoast where I was last summer. It would be a perfect hideout for pirates. Wild and rugged and lonely. I intend to write a yarn about it someday."

Henley had raised himself on one elbow. He was staring at Stevenson with hungry eyes. His long stay in the hospital had left him starved for another writer's company.

"You could put it on the stage. It would make a rare play," he told Stevenson.

Louis shook his head. "A book, I think. One to draw children from play and old men from the chimney corner."

Rodden and Willie, the two young boys in the ward, stared open-mouthed at the speakers. Here were two grown men who were actually talking sense. Instead of useless words about money, business, or the weather, they were discussing pirates!

For the better part of the afternoon, the big man in the bed and the slender one in the chair talked without stopping. No pirate

who ever lived was left out — Captain Kidd,
Captain Teach (also known as Blackbeard),
Captain Blood, and all the other rascals who
sailed the Spanish Main. Between the two
of them, they spun tales that left the listening
youngsters reeling and breathless.

Leslie Stephen sat quietly by. He was delighted with the success of the visit. At last he
reached over and touched Louis on the
shoulder.

"We should be going. Dr. Lister will not
like it if we overstay our time."

The light went out of Henley's eyes. "So
soon? It seems as though you had just
come."

"I'll be back," Louis promised. "I'll be
back soon. I'll bring you a stack of books
and magazines."

Outside in the corridor Louis shook his
head. "It does not seem right that the sun
shines so brightly when *he* is a prisoner in a
hospital bed."

"He is a brave man," Mr. Stephen agreed.
"He has suffered from a disease of the bone

103

since he was a small child. He has already lost one foot. He may still lose the other, but the great Dr. Lister thinks he can save it. The treatments are very painful. Henley has already been in the hospital for eighteen months, but he never complains."

"He may be lame and helpless, but he reminds me of a king," Louis said. "I intend to do what I can to make his days more bearable."

The young Scot was as good as his word. He took Henley books of his own. He borrowed books from his friends to take to the hospital. One day, being short of money — he usually was — he carried an easy chair through the streets of Edinburgh for his friend.

When spring came, Louis begged permission of Dr. Lister to take his patient out in the Stevenson carriage.

On the day of the ride, Louis ran up the infirmary stairs two at a time and into the long ward where Henley was waiting. Louis's long, thin face was glowing.

"The carriage is waiting!" he announced. "Let's be off. We mustn't waste a moment. It's spring outside!"

Henley had been dressed for an hour. His crutch was by his side. He had limped up and down the hall as often as the attendants would allow. But now that the time had come, he seemed unwilling to go.

"There's not an orderly in sight, lad," he sighed. "I'll never make it down the long stairs without help."

"Stuff and nonsense," Louis scoffed. "I'm here."

Henley glanced at his friend's slight form and then looked at his own huge frame. Both young men burst out laughing.

"Come on," Louis urged. "We can do it."

The passage downstairs was difficult. Several times Henley leaned on him until Stevenson's shoulder felt as though it would give way. But, inch by inch, they made their way out to the street and into the carriage.

Henley leaned back against the cushions. Louis nodded to the driver. The carriage

rolled slowly through the Edinburgh streets.

Louis looked across at his golden-bearded friend. There were actually tears in the eyes that usually shone with laughter.

"My dear boy, I'll never forget this. Never!" Henley said in husky tones. "I am in debt to you for life."

CHAPTER 10

A Canoe Trip

During spring vacation Louis crossed the Channel to France where Bob was staying with a group of art students on the edge of the Forest of Fontainebleau (*fon tehn bloh'*). Those were perfect days. Louis was happy with the friendly young art students. He like their careless style of dress and their gay, informal meals at Siron's Inn. For several weeks he visited with Bob at the little village of Barbizon. He made notes for an essay about the Forest of Fontainebleau, for everything Louis saw or did turned into words sooner or later.

At last he realized he must return home. His final law exams were near at hand. He must forget his writing and settle down to studying for several weeks. He felt very sad when the time came to leave his carefree friends at Barbizon.

Bob clapped him on the shoulder. "Don't look so unhappy!"

"How can I help it?" Louis exclaimed. "You will be here in the warm sunshine, and I shall be in foggy Edinburgh."

Bob shrugged. "You wanted to be a lawyer, didn't you?"

"No," Louis said in a decided manner. "But it's better than being an engineer. At least I shall have a few free hours now and then to write."

In July, 1875, Robert Louis Stevenson became a lawyer. He would be twenty-five on his next birthday. But in spite of his age, he was still a boy at heart.

Thomas Stevenson and his wife had driven down into the city in their open carriage in honor of the day Louis was to become a lawyer. After the ceremony, Louis, dressed in a black suit, joined them when the speeches were over.

The Castle clock struck the hour of twelve

as their carriage rolled homeward. The
streets were filled with the usual noonday
crowd.

Louis rode on the folded top of the carriage while his parents sat in the seat. He
was overjoyed. The long, tiresome task was
over. For once he had pleased his father.

Every time he saw someone he knew, he
cupped his hands to his mouth and whooped
the good news.

"I'm a lawyer at last — just passed my
exams!"

At first his mother was horrified. "Louis!
What will people think?"

His father laughed. "Let him celebrate.
He would shout louder if he knew I had
put a thousand pounds for him in the bank."

Louis turned unbelieving eyes upon him.
His allowance had always been smaller than
that of any of his friends. A thousand pounds
(five thousand dollars) sounded like a fortune.

"Hurrah!" he cried. "I'm rich!"

As time passed, neither Louis nor his father

111

remained happy about his job. He soon turned his back on it and spent all his time writing. Thomas Stevenson was greatly disappointed. He had hoped that time would cure his son of wanting to be an author. Meanwhile, in Louis's hands, the thousand pounds grew smaller fast. He had too many friends always in need of money.

In the autumn of 1876, Louis planned a canoe trip with Walter Simpson. By this time France was Louis's adopted country. He spoke the language like a native. In France he found the freedom which until now had escaped him. He had many friends at Barbizon. Here would end the journey which Walter and he had planned.

They were a lighthearted pair as they set off from Antwerp with their canoes, the *Cigarette* and the *Arethusa* (*air ee thoo' zah*). Their route lay by way of Brussels. From there they would proceed into France and down the River Oise (*wahz*) to Grez (*gray*). This was a little town where Bob now stayed. It was only a few miles from Barbizon.

The journey was a time Stevenson would later make famous in *An Inland Voyage*. The two had many adventures. Louis narrowly escaped drowning once when his canoe upset.

Walter pushed on ahead of Louis, and he came into port several hours before his companion.

The September sun was setting as Louis guided the *Arethusa* skillfully down the river. His keen eyes searched the bank. The landing at Grez must be near.

Ah! there it was. He paddled toward the shore.

A small, solemn-faced boy was seated on the shore. He watched Louis drag his canoe above the water line.

"Hello, young fellow," Louis called.

The boy continued to stare. He saw a tall, thin young man whose face was tanned by the sun and the wind. He was dressed in boating trousers and a wrinkled velveteen jacket. A small cap was perched on the top of his longer-than-usual yellow hair.

"Hello," the straight-faced boy said at last.

"You waited long enough," Louis said with a grin. "I trust I meet with your approval."

"Oh, yes," the boy said with childish honesty. "You do. And so does your boat."

Louis threw a careless glance at the canoe. "I rather fancy it myself. I'll take you for a ride sometime. That is, if your mother will allow you to go."

"She will," the boy told him.

Louis's eyes twinkled. "You seem very certain."

"She will let me do anything I want to do as long as it doesn't hurt me," the boy said gravely.

"Very good," Louis replied. "Very good, indeed. And where is this unusual lady?"

The boy nodded toward the inn where voices and laughter came from the open windows. "She's in there with the other artists."

Louis raised his eyebrows. "Women artists? At Grez?"

"Only my mother and my sister Belle."

By now Louis was striding up the slope. The boy ran along at his heels.

"What's your name?" Louis asked.

"Sam Lloyd Osbourne," the youngster replied. "They usually call me Pettifish in the village. What do they call you?"

"Lou Stevenson."

The boy gave a whistle. "You must be Bob's cousin. He told us all about you."

"Not *all,* I hope," Louis laughed.

"Everything," Lloyd insisted. "You are his favorite cousin. You aren't very strong. You write well, and you paint a little. You have passed your law exams, but you don't care for the law. Mother thinks you sound interesting."

Louis did not hear the boy's last words. He had reached the porch of the inn and stood looking in at one of the long dining room windows.

A dozen or more guests were gathered about the big table inside. They were eating, drinking, and talking. They did not see Louis until he called out to them. They gave

116

a shout as they looked up and saw him framed in the window with the sunset at his back.

"Lou!"

He leaped across the window sill and was in the room. His mischievous, wide-set eyes gleamed like stars as he made a mocking bow.

"It's about time you came," Walter Simpson said. "I wondered what had become of you. I'd about decided you'd found a watery grave."

Louis shook his head. "I shall die in a ditch — with my boots on."

But he was not looking at Walter. He was looking past him at one of the two women seated at the table. He saw Fanny Van de-Grift Osbourne, the lovely young mother of Lloyd and Belle. Louis couldn't take his eyes from her face. Before either of them had spoken a word, Louis was in love with her.

There's no music like a little river's. It plays the same tune (and that's the favorite) over and over again, and yet does not weary of it like men fiddlers. It takes the mind out of doors; and though we should be grateful for good houses, there is, after all, no house like God's out-of-doors.

from *Prince Otto*

CHAPTER 11

Young Artists
at Grez

The days at Grez were golden ones. Louis carried Fanny Osbourne's painting easel whenever she went into the woods. He became fast friends with her son and daughter. Young Belle wrote to a friend that he was the nicest "ugly man" she had ever known. Lloyd never grew tired of his stories. Louis never seemed to tire of telling them.

The ones the boy liked best were taken from Scottish history and from *Pilgrim's Progress*. Lloyd thought Louis was the best storyteller he had ever heard. Secretly he gave his new friend the name of Great-Heart from the character in John Bunyan's book.

The carefree artists stayed outdoors every minute the weather permitted. They found time to play as well as to work. Their favorite game was mock war, which they played in their canoes. They were as much at home on the water as on the land.

When the rain spoiled their sport, they gathered in the dining room of the inn and played parlor games. They were all young, happy, and gay.

Perhaps the times that Louis liked best were those when Fanny and he sat alone by the fire and talked far into the night. She could talk, and she could listen. He had never been so happy.

When she was with Louis, Fanny forgot her troubles. She forgot that she had little money to rear her two children from a previous marriage. She forgot that she was several years older than Stevenson. She lived one day at a time and was as deeply in love with Louis as he was with her.

The summer ended. Louis went home to Edinburgh and the practice of the law. But he did not remain in Scotland long. France and Fanny called him.

In February he was in Paris for a short time. Then another summer came, and he was back at Grez. Of course, the Osbournes were there, too. By this time he was writing the story of last summer's voyage that had ended at Grez.

When autumn came, Louis was often in London. Henley was there. He was editor of a magazine, although he had to hobble about on crutches to do his work. Louis began a series of stories, *New Arabian Nights,* for his friend's magazine.

Whenever Louis went to Paris, he lived in the old part of the city where living was cheap. It was a dingy spot, but Fanny was nearby. She had returned from Grez to her Paris apartment.

In the summer of 1878, he was secretary to a former engineering professor who was head of the International Exhibit, which was held in Paris. The job made it possible for him to be near the Osbourne family.

At the end of the summer Fanny and her children went to London. They were on their way to America. Louis returned to London with them. He became very busy with his work for Henley and Henley's magazine, the *London*. Indeed, many people think that a large part of Louis's thousand pounds helped to make the magazine possible.

The time came for Fanny's boat to sail. Louis said good-by to her and the children in August.

A few weeks after they had left, he went off alone for a tramp in the mountains of France. His only companion was a small, mouse-colored donkey named Modestine. He made her famous in *Travels with a Donkey*.

He started on his journey on a fine September day with Modestine, a sleeping bag, and more baggage than man and donkey could carry comfortably. Together the two shared many adventures. Modestine turned out to be stubborn, but Louis grew fond of her.

In twelve days' time he tramped a hundred and twenty miles. At the end of that time he sold Modestine. He returned home by stage coach. He was calmer, healthier, and happier — and still in love with Fanny.

Louis went back to London. He threw himself again into work for Henley's magazine, but his mind was far, far away in California with Fanny.

For months he wrestled with his problems. He was poor. He made only a few dollars now and then on his writing. The thousand pounds from his father was gone. How could he support Fanny and her children? He had never supported even himself.

Then one day in August, 1879, nearly a year after she had sailed for America, he received a cablegram from Fanny. She was ill and needed him.

Without telling his parents, he booked passage on an emigrant ship to America.

CHAPTER 12

Ill, but Happy, in America

Louis did not sail for America in a happy mood. It hurt him to leave his father and mother without saying good-by to them. But he knew that sharing his plans with them would lead only to more quarrels. He had had enough of quarrels. He was on his way to Fanny. No one could stop him.

In *The Amateur Emigrant,* he relates the story of his voyage. He went second-class because he had very little money. In his book he tells of the noise, the smells, and the bad food. His great liking for people of all kinds peeps through every line. He always felt better on sea than on land, and the journey was not too bad. He had time to finish *The Story of a Lie,* which he had begun months earlier. He sent this to Sidney Colvin as soon as the boat docked in America. He hoped his friend would find a publisher for it. He knew he would need the money before long.

The sea voyage was better than the trip to come. The journey across the continent was horrible. But, as usual, his experiences produced a book. He called it *Across the Plains.*

Louis had already been a sick man when he left England. Up to that time he had been a pampered only child. For the first time in his life, he had no one to whom he could turn.

The slow train on which he traveled had many discomforts. There were no berths. The passengers slept at night on rough boards stretched across the aisles from one wooden bench to another. There was no dining car. The passengers bought food at wayside stations when they were fortunate enough to be first in line. Often the food gave out before the last passengers could reach the counter. Louis missed many a meal because he felt so ill that he could not push his way to the front.

Eleven days of this travel weakened him. When he reached San Francisco, he learned that Fanny was now living in Monterey. By this time his money had run out.

On the way to Monterey he fell ill and was nursed by an old hunter. Finally he reached the town and collapsed at the door of a cafe owner, Jules Simoneau (*see moh noh'*). Simoneau proved a true friend to Louis Stevenson.

For three months Louis lived in poor quarters on poor food. He wrote like a madman to make money. He should have made more, but his friends in London were determined to bring him back across the ocean. Colvin and Henley wrote him that they thought poorly of *The Amateur Emigrant* and *Travels with a Donkey*. He answered:

127

Everybody writes me sermons; it's . . . hardly the food necessary for a man who lives all alone on forty-five cents a day, and sometimes less, with quantities of hard work and many heavy thoughts. If one of you could write me a letter with a jest in it — I am still flesh and blood —"

But he was not unhappy all the time. He saw Fanny every day. He was a welcome visitor at the rose-covered cottage where she lived with a younger sister, Nellie Van de-Grift, and Lloyd, who was now a long-legged boy of twelve. Belle had eloped with a young artist named Joe Strong.

In December Louis followed Fanny to San Francisco. Here the tuberculosis which had threatened him all his life caught up with him. Poor lodgings, not enough food, sleepless nights, and worry were largely responsible. He wavered for a time between life and death. It was during this period that he wrote an early version of the famous *Requiem*.

Fanny Osbourne nursed him day and night. As soon as he was able to be on his feet, Louis and Fanny were quietly married. He was still very ill, however. That was May, 1880.

Meanwhile Fanny had been busy. She had sent letters to his friends in England, telling of his serious condition. His father wired him money. He wrote that his son could count on two hundred and fifty pounds a year from him. Fortune, at least for the time, seemed to be turning in his favor.

Louis and Fanny took Lloyd up in the mountains of California to a deserted silver mine. Here they camped out for two months. Louis began to feel better. Even with his new happiness, he still found time to write. This book was *The Silverado Squatters,* the story of their honeymoon.

By now, letters were traveling between Scotland and California. His parents wanted him to bring his wife and stepson home.

In August, 1880, the three sailed from New York. A great deal had happened since Fanny's cablegram to Louis a year before.

Fanny Speaks Up

All the Stevensons were to-
gether at last in the dining room at 17 Heriot
Row. Thomas Stevenson smiled down the
long table at his wife, Margaret. His new
daughter-in-law Fanny sat at his right. Louis
on her other side was next to his mother at
the foot of the table. Lloyd had a whole
side to himself and was very glad of it. He
had a better chance to sneak food to Woggs,
the black Skye terrier. Woggs was a recent
present to Louis from his boyhood friend,
Walter Simpson.

As soon as the boat had docked at Liver-
pool, the Stevenson family had gone directly
to the mountains of Scotland. The climate
had not agreed with Louis. The damp
Scotland climate had never been good for him.

His uncle George, who was also his doctor, had ordered him to Switzerland for the winter.

But tonight they all wanted to make their first dinner at home a happy occasion. Although Louis wished he did not have to go to Switzerland, his heart warmed every time he looked at Fanny. No place could be too bad if she were there.

He was glad to be home once more. He had missed the old surroundings. The banquet table with its spotless linens, gleaming crystal, and shining silver was a sharp contrast to some of his eating places in America.

Mr. Stevenson was annoyed by the maid. She was new, and she was clumsy. He liked faultless service. He was not a patient man.

"Hold the bread plate where I can reach it," he snapped.

The girl trembled. "Yes, sir," she faltered.

A few minutes later he scowled at her. "Can't you see it's time to pass the potatoes?"

The serving maid's hands shook. "Yes, sir."

"Yes, sir. Yes, sir," he repeated. "Must you say 'yes, sir' every time I speak to you?"

The girl hastily set the dish down on the table and fled, weeping, to the kitchen. All eyes at the table were fixed on the swinging door through which she had disappeared.

Fanny rose from her chair. Her napkin was tightly clutched in her fist. She glared at her father-in-law. Sparks fairly flew from her dark eyes.

"If you speak like that once more to a poor servant girl who doesn't dare to answer back, I shall go to my room and stay there," she announced.

Thomas Stevenson stared at her in unbelief. He was not used to having his behavior questioned.

Louis was the first of the group to find his voice. "My wife always speaks her mind, Father," he said with amusement in his voice.

But the elder Stevenson did not hear him. He was laughing heartily and patting Fanny's small hand that lay on the table.

"I doubt ye're a besom," he said in broad Scots. "That means a bossy woman, child. You would never be one, but anyone hearing your speech just now might accuse you of it. I know better, for I've watched you with Louis. You lead him, but you never drive him. I like your spirit. You're a woman after my own heart, Fanny. As for me, my bark is worse than my bite. And I'm more than passing glad you married my son."

Fanny gave him a startled smile. "And I'm glad, too, that I married him. Aside from the fact that I love him, it's good to be here."

She waved a hand to include the long table and the people around it. "I have not always led an easy life. It's good to be a part of the Stevenson clan."

Her father-in-law gave her hand a final pat. "That you are, lass," he assured her.

He liked this little woman who dared to say what she thought.

Soon Louis, Fanny, Lloyd, and Woggs left for Davos (*dah vohs'*) in the Swiss Alps. Louis, who loved warmth and sunshine, went unwillingly. He never admitted that he was an invalid. He did not choose to be surrounded by invalids. And Davos was a town of invalids.

Woggs and Lloyd helped to make life bearable for him there. They, at least, were young. They were a tie with the world outside. They were no part of the sick people who were prisoners in the little health resort.

Lloyd knew that money — or the lack of it — was a constant source of worry to his mother and Louis.

Again and again the boy would hear his

stepfather say: "Fanny, I shall have to write to my father."

One day the boy decided he had found a way to help. After a mysterious absence of a few hours, he proudly displayed a handful of small coins to Louis.

"Why, you're rich!" the other said. "Where did you get all that money?"

Lloyd beamed. "I'm printing programs on my old printing press for the weekly entertainments. I have an agreement with the manager."

Louis's eyes met Fanny's over the boy's

head. There was pride in his voice. "You have two men instead of one, my dear."

When spring came, they were glad to escape from Davos. By late summer the elder Mr. and Mrs. Stevenson were staying with them in a cottage at Braemar (*bray mahr'*). The town was the royal summer residence. Every day the members of the Stevenson household watched Queen Victoria ride by in her carriage with her ladies-in-waiting.

Louis was ill much of the time. In fancy he went back to his childhood and wrote some of the verses we know today as *A Child's Garden of Verses*. He thought at the time he wrote them that *Penny Whistles* would be a good title.

But another book was started at Braemar. Lloyd was home from boarding school. He had no companions his own age. Louis Stevenson might be a boy at heart, but for the time being, he was buried deep in law books and papers. He had applied for a post in law at the University of Edinburgh!

Meanwhile Lloyd wandered about with

Woggs at his heels. At last Stevenson took pity on the boy's unhappy state. He held out a hand to see a picture Lloyd was painting.

"It's an island," his stepson explained, looking over Stevenson's shoulder.

"Hm-m," Stevenson commented. He made a few swift strokes with his pen here and there. "It looks like a fat dragon standing up. Let's put in a few swashbuckling names for luck," he added gleefully. "Here is Spyglass Hill, and here is Skeleton Island."

Before long he sat down at his desk with a stack of white paper before him. His pen flew. Fanny, glancing in at the door, shook her head at Lloyd. When her husband was in that mood, it meant that he must not be disturbed.

After the evening meal, as the family sat about the fireside, he brought out a sheaf of papers.

"I began a pirate tale today. Would you like to hear it?" he asked. His eyes were on Lloyd. *The Seacook,* as Stevenson called it, was written especially for him.

" 'Squire Trelawney, Dr. Livesey, and the rest of these gentlemen, having asked me to write down the whole particulars about Treasure Island . . . I take my pen in the year of grace 17——, and go back to the time when my father kept the Admiral Benbow Inn,' " he began.

Those are the familiar words of *Treasure Island,* which schoolboys and schoolgirls have been reading ever since the evening when Stevenson's wife, stepson, and parents were the first to hear them.

They were charmed by the story. Thomas Stevenson seemed as interested as Lloyd. It was he who suggested the apple barrel on the deck of the *Hispaniola* (*ee spahn yoh' lah*) as a place for the young hero, Jim Hawkins, to hide when he discovered the pirates' plot.

The book contains one of the great villains of all time. Not everyone knows that Long John Silver (the seacook) is Stevenson's friend Henley, stripped of all his finer qualities. As a villain he still has his strength, courage, and marked enjoyment of life.

139

Every night Stevenson's family gathered to hear the next chapter of the story. At this time the author's health was especially poor. He had to spend the whole day in bed. That did not stop his magic pen. It only made the hours pass faster for him.

A friend who heard the story before it was finished insisted that he send it to the editor of a boy's magazine called *Young Folks*. The editor read a sample and promptly accepted it.

The story was completed at Davos where he was forced to spend a second winter. He wrote at breakneck speed and before long completed the manuscript.

Of course, he dedicated it to Lloyd:

To
Lloyd Osbourne
An American Gentleman
In accordance with whose classic taste
The following narrative has been designed
It is now, in return for the numerous delightful hours
And with the kindest wishes, dedicated
by his affectionate friend
The Author

This second winter at Davos was a little easier to bear than the first had been. The Stevensons, with Lloyd and Woggs, rented a small house, the Chalet am Stein (*shah lay' ahm styne*). Here in the attic "General Stevenson" and "General Osbourne" played at endless games of war with lead soldiers.

Lloyd wrote and printed a small book called *Black Canyon: or Life in the Far West*. It was illustrated with woodcuts that had come with the press.

Stevenson wanted to share in the fun. He submitted some poems to the young editor. Lloyd published fifty copies of them and paid his stepfather three francs in royalties.

The man and the boy enjoyed all this. They needed new woodcuts for their next project. A Swiss invalid made a dozen of them. The little printing press hammered away. The result was *Moral Emblems: A Collection of Cuts and Verses*. It sold for sixpence a copy. Today these tiny booklets with their saucy verses are collector's items.

CHAPTER 14

Stevenson Writes
in Bed

The next year found the Louis Stevensons at Hyères (*yer*) in France in a tiny house on a hillside. Stevenson named it Chalet La Solitude (*shah lay' lah soh lee tewd'*). Years later he wrote: "I was happy only once; that was at Hyères."

Life was very sweet to him during those months. He was recognized now as a writer of promise. He was hard at work on *Penny Whistles (A Child's Garden of Verses)*. He was continuing *Prince Otto,* which he had begun back in California.

At Hyères he began to write *The Black Arrow* for the magazine that had published

Treasure Island. The Black Arrow is a tale of the Wars of the Roses in England during the Middle Ages. About this time an editor wanted to bring out *Treasure Island* in book form. He paid Stevenson a hundred pounds for the book rights. For the first time in his life Stevenson was making a living instead of taking money from his father.

Friends from England came often to Chalet La Solitude. Sometimes Fanny thought they came too often. On the other hand, they felt that she guarded her husband like a dragon. Perhaps she did, but she knew that little lay between him and death. His friends refused to treat him like the sick man he was, and too often he acted like a naughty boy.

Henley and a friend named Baxter came for Christmas, 1883. Some time after Christmas Day, the three men decided to go to Nice for further celebration.

The trip was too much for Stevenson. He almost died. Fanny came rushing to nurse him. She took him back to Hyères, where

144

he lay near death for months. At times he was forbidden to speak a word.

During these dark days he wrote most of the gay verses in *A Child's Garden of Verses*. There is no hint of the sick room or odor of medicine bottles about them. The very breath of childhood clings to them. In rising above the shadow of ill health, he was proving himself a gentleman who was not afraid to die.

During their stay at Hyères the Stevensons secured the services of a French-Swiss girl named Valentine Roch. She was more like a member of the family than like a maid, just as Cummy had been long ago.

When Stevenson finally improved, the family returned to England. Thomas Stevenson, who was in failing health, made Louis a present of a house at Bournemouth (*born' muth*) which had been the home of a retired navy officer. The Stevensons renamed the house Skerryvore for the most famous lighthouse Louis's father had built.

Stevenson placed a model lighthouse at the

entrance to their new home. It was lighted every evening and cast its beams up and down the street.

The Stevensons were very proud of Skerryvore. There was room for Woggs to run. There was a big yellow cat. There were cooing pigeons.

And inside —

"Our drawing room is now a place so beautiful that it is like eating to sit in it. No other room is so lovely in the world; there I sit like an old . . . beggarman . . . in a palace throne room."

Some good writing came into being at Skerryvore. He was forced to write in bed most of the time. There he wrote "Markheim," "Olalla," and other stories. There he set down *Kidnapped,* which many readers prefer to *Treasure Island.* Louis himself liked it better.

But the great work was *Dr. Jekyll and Mr. Hyde.* For three days he wrote furiously at the rate of ten thousand words a day. Then he read it aloud to Fanny and Lloyd. His stepson approved the story of the well-known doctor by day who became a misshapen monster by night. But Fanny shook her head. It was only a thriller. Every human being has something of Dr. Jekyll and Mr. Hyde in him, she said.

Louis threw the manuscript angrily into the fire. Then he worked without stopping for three more days. The result was the book as we know it.

It was printed and caught on slowly. Then more and more people began to read it. Parts of it were read from pulpits. It was talked about on street corners. It lay on the tables of most of the homes in Britain. Its author was a success, at last.

Thomas Stevenson, who had been ill for a long time, was steadily growing worse. He died in 1887. The tie that had bound Louis Stevenson to Scotland and England was broken. At last he was free to seek a warmer, milder climate. He made up his mind to go to America and the mountains of the West.

CHAPTER 15

Another Writer
in the Family

On August 22, 1887, the Stevensons — Louis, his mother, Fanny, Lloyd, and their maid, Valentine Roch, sailed for America. They went on a cargo boat in order to save money on transportation. It docked at Le Havre (*luh ah' vr*), France, to take on a load of apes and horses. To everyone's amusement, Jocko, a pet ape, took a fancy to Stevenson.

The crossing was rough. The old boat rolled like a "great bucket of iron." Fanny and Valentine were poor sailors. But Lloyd and "Aunt Maggie," as everyone except her son Louis called her, found their sea legs at once. Stevenson was all over the ship from stem to stern. He laughed and joked and made friends with all on board, including the animals.

The voyage was a release from the prison which his stay at Skerryvore had proved. Always better at sea, he rejoiced in his newly found freedom. "I had forgotten what happiness was. . . . My heart literally sang," he wrote to Bob.

To his surprise, New York gave him a royal welcome. *Dr. Jekyll and Mr. Hyde* had made him famous in America. It was even playing on the stage.

Stevenson did not like crowds and reporters, but he liked the growing income that his spreading fame had brought him. He signed an agreement with Charles Scribner, whose book company wanted to bring out a new edition of *Treasure Island*. They also wanted him to write twelve articles for *Scribner's* magazine at three hundred dollars apiece. In addition, Mr. Scribner offered him eight thousand dollars if Stevenson would promise to let Scribner print his next book. And he had once thought twelve hundred dollars a year a fair income!

Settled at last in a New York hotel, Stevenson looked up from his bed at his wife. Much against his will, he was resting. He had caught a bad cold on the ship, and now it threatened to make him really ill. But his spirits never dragged. Although his eyes had dark circles beneath them, they were dancing with glee.

"I feel exactly like the old woman in the nursery rhyme. You remember — the one who said: 'Lawk-a-mercy! Lawk-a-mercy! Can this be I?' Only, of course, our cases are a little different. I believe she was crying over the loss of her petticoat. Now, I never stop wondering at my change from rags to riches. Seven years ago I was sailing for England with Lloyd and you. I was only a poor skeleton, dependent on my father for money for our trip home. Now I'm only a skeleton. But at least I am making our living."

"Of course you are," Fanny said. She looked anxiously at his too-rosy cheeks. " I must get you away from all these people. You probably caught this miserable cold from one of them."

"Pizen sarpints," Louis agreed.

A little smile passed between them. These words were their private joke. It was their term for persons with colds who Fanny was quite sure would give them to Louis.

"Where shall we go?" she asked. "There must be a place, if I only knew it."

"They say Saranac Lake, New York, up in the Adirondack Mountains is a good spot for folks like me," Louis suggested.

So to Saranac Lake they went. The weather was cold in the mountains near the Canadian border, even in October. The family of five lived in a little frame cottage on a windy hilltop. Fanny went off to Canada and came back with fur coats and caps to keep them warm.

Louis felt wonderful. He went straight to work on the stories for Mr. Scribner which would begin in the January issue of his magazine. One of them was *The Lantern Bearers*. It took its name from the sport of his boyhood days in the seashore town of North Berwick long ago.

His big work for the winter was *The Master of Ballantrae*. He threw himself into the story eagerly. In spite of this task, however, he found time to work with Lloyd (who wrote because his hero, his stepfather, was writing) on *The Wrong Box*.

Meanwhile the weather became so cold that the thermometer dropped to ten below zero. The snowdrifts piled up outside. The ink froze in the bottle. Poor Fanny fled to her girlhood home, Indianapolis. There, at least, she could find a better built house than the little cottage on the hill at Saranac Lake. Besides, mountain heights never agreed with her. Later she went to California to visit her sister Nellie.

By that time she had another reason for crossing the country. Mr. McClure of the New York *Sun* had asked Stevenson to make a voyage among the South Sea Islands and write travel letters about them.

Stevenson was getting bored with Saranac Lake. He had never liked to stay in one place long. Since his arrival in America, he had thought of little but going to sea again. Here was his chance. Out came the atlas. Out came the maps.

"There will be hundreds of miles of nothing but ocean." Lloyd said, looking over his shoulder.

"Good," his stepfather answered. "I'm more at home on water than on land. And there will be new scenes, new faces, new ways of living. I get awfully tired of the same old thing. I shall write Fanny to look for a boat when she goes to visit Nellie."

He closed the atlas with a bang. "Lloyd, we're as good as on our way. When your mother sets out to do something, it's as good as done. And, Hurrah! there won't be any snow in the South Seas."

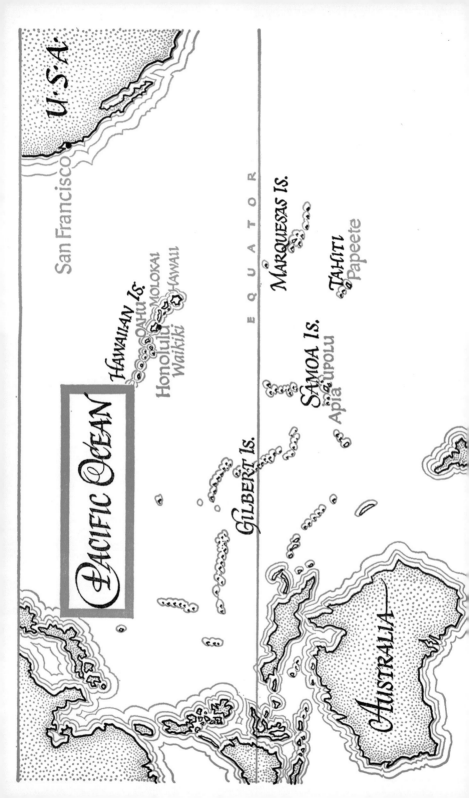

CHAPTER 16

Stevenson Buys
a Jungle

Soon after her arrival in California, Fanny telegraphed that she had found a boat. The *Casco* belonged to a wealthy doctor who was willing to rent it to the Stevensons.

In June, 1888, the *Casco* set sail with Louis, Fanny, Lloyd, Aunt Maggie, Valentine, and Captain Otis. Belle Strong waved good-by to them from the San Francisco wharf. She was there on a visit from Honolulu, where she, her artist husband, and their little boy Austin now lived. Later the Stevensons planned to join them in Hawaii. But a long trip was in store for the *Casco* first.

The first stopping place was the Marquesas (*mahr kay' suhs*), a group of islands three thousand miles away in the Pacific. Captain Otis brought the *Casco* into port on an outlying island exactly thirty days after the boat had steamed away from the wharf at San Francisco.

The ship had hardly dropped anchor when brown-skinned natives in canoes swarmed out to meet them. At first these natives were angry because the strangers in the big boat would not buy their fruit and baskets. Then Stevenson won them with gifts of salt beef, biscuits, and sugar from the ship's store.

For three weeks the party explored the island by day and slept on the boat at night. Stevenson made many notes about native habits before they moved on to another group of islands. Then he caught a cold. He was quite ill by the time they reached Papeete (*pah pih yay' tay*).

Fanny managed to get him moved to more comfortable quarters in a village. Here she and her husband made friends with Princess

Möe, a kindly Polynesian princess. Under her care Stevenson began to improve. Ori, the village chief, also became a friend. Later Stevenson said of these natives: "God's best — at least God's sweetest works — Polynesians."

Meanwhile the captain of the *Casco* discovered that his craft was full of dry rot. He went back to Papeete for repairs. For weeks Louis and his family were alone with the natives, who were wonderfully kind to them. When the white strangers' food gave out, their friends gave them raw fish with coconut milk and roasted bananas.

At last the boat returned. On Christmas Day the Stevensons sailed for Honolulu, where Belle and Joe Strong were waiting.

In Honolulu Captain Otis said good-by to the Stevensons and sailed back with the *Casco* to San Francisco. This had been the plan from the beginning.

Mail from England told Stevenson that he still had a large bank account. This fact took a load of worry from his mind.

He rented a house on the beach at Waikiki (*wy kih kee'*) for his family. Here he finished *The Master of Ballantrae* and rewrote *The Wrong Box*. Here he studied Hawaiian and wrote poems about the Polynesians. The islands were beginning to cast their spell upon him.

Through Belle and Joe, the Stevensons became well acquainted with King Kalakaua (*kah lah kah yu' ah*), the native Hawaiian king, and his sister, the Princess Liliuokalani (*lee lee woh kah lah' nee*). Stevenson and the king soon became fast friends. The royal carriage was often seen outside the Stevenson residence.

Finally the time came to leave Hawaii. The Stevensons intended to cruise awhile longer among the South Sea Islands. But first Stevenson made another visit.

While Fanny waited for him, he went to the leper settlement on the island of Molokai (*moh loh kah' ee*). Lepers from the surrounding area were sent to that island for life. Fanny, with a sinking heart, saw Louis

160

off on the trip. At the last minute she brought her husband a pair of gloves.

"You will wear them, won't you?" she begged.

He shook his head. "They have enough to bear without that!"

For eight days he lived among the unfortunate people. He chatted with the old beachcombers. He played croquet with the leper children. He promised to send the little girls scraps to make doll dresses — and he kept his word. When he left the island, he had a new name to place high on his list of heroes — Father Damien, the Catholic priest who had died of leprosy only a few weeks before Stevenson's visit.

Upon his return to Honolulu, Fanny and he sailed on a trading schooner for the Gilbert Islands. By now Aunt Maggie had gone home to nurse her sick sister. Valentine Roch had left also. She had decided to return to the United States.

Joe Strong went with the Stevensons. And Lloyd was along. Belle and little Austin

were sent to Australia to wait for them.

It was a rough voyage, but Stevenson stayed strong and well. Perhaps the highlight of the journey was their friendship with the savage king of Abemama (*ah bay mah' mah*). He was a fierce man who shot at anyone he did not like. Fortunately, he liked Stevenson.

Toward the end of the journey the boat docked at Apia (*ah pee' ah*) on the island of Upolu (*oo poh' loo*) in the Samoan Islands. This was a colony of three hundred white men.

Here the party left the boat, which sailed on its way. Land looked good to the passengers who had been on the water for five months. They decided to settle down for a long stay before they booked passage back to Australia.

Then something important happened. Louis decided to buy a plantation on this tropical island and to build a house. Here he could avoid the English winters that had never agreed with him. Fanny hoped he

163

would follow through with the plan. With her "green thumb," she was certain that the plantation would be profitable. She hoped that the money from the crops would lift some of the load from her husband's shoulders.

Stevenson became the owner of three hundred acres of land on a mountain above Apia. It was a wooded jungle, but it was all his.

Now he was eager to get back to Australia and the mailbag. This, he thought, would be only the first stage of his journey back to England. He had not seen his friends there for two and a half years.

At length the Stevensons left Apia and the tropics. They sailed for Australia.

In Australia Stevenson caught a cold almost at once. For the first time since Papeete, he was very ill. Fanny feared she would never get him on his feet again.

Both felt that he would get well if he could get to sea. Fanny persuaded the captain of a trading vessel to take them aboard. Slowly Louis began to recover. During the

months on the tramp steamer Stevenson and
Fanny began to realize that he must stay in
a tropical climate if he wanted to remain alive.
And Stevenson wanted to remain alive, for he
loved life as few men do.

CHAPTER 17

Life at Vailima

When the news reached England that Stevenson did not intend to return, the letters came pouring in. His friends half a world away could not understand his decision and said so.

But Fanny and he knew what they were doing. In the South Seas he was strong and happy. In any other climate he was an invalid with death just around the corner. He had no choice. For him it was a matter of life and death.

All the rest of his life he was homesick at times for his "ain gray town" of Edinburgh, but he knew that for him Samoa must be home forever.

When Fanny and he returned to Apia, they found that their agent had cleared a jungle path and built a house of sorts on their mountain acres.

Now they set to work with a will. Although they had native boys to help them, they did much of the actual labor themselves. There was land to be cleared. There was a permanent house to be built. There was planting to be done. There were stables, pig-pens, cattle sheds, poultry houses to be raised. A real road must be built down to the little town on the seacoast.

Meanwhile in the midst of all the hustle and bustle, Stevenson discovered that he was no longer an invalid. He swung an axe and cleared the jungle as if he were a seasoned pioneer. He felt as though he were living in a fairy tale. Instead of spending his days in bed, he lived outdoors much of the time. He even rode horseback.

There was plenty of time to write. He worked for hours each day on the travel letters he had promised Mr. McClure. Meanwhile work on the new house continued. Louis knew he must work hard to pay for it. By this time Fanny and he had named their new home Vailima (*vy lee' muh* — Five Rivers).

As the weeks went by, all the family gathered there. His mother came first. He went to Australia to meet her. Then the Strongs arrived with Austin. Finally Lloyd came with the furniture and household goods from England. Now the circle was almost complete.

Not quite complete, though. Stevenson was a Scot through and through. He had a Highlander's love for the clan. The simple, childlike Samoans loved him. Before long the staff at Vailima included a native gardener, a cattle boy, a cook, and numerous other native workers. All of them were proud to be a part of the family of *Tusitala* (*tu see tah' lah* — Storyteller, or Teller of Tales). It was natural for him to send across the ocean for tartan plaids for his brown-skinned brothers. If he could not return to his homeland, then he would bring his homeland to Samoa.

The Samoan natives gave special names to

the Stevenson family. The name of *Tusitala* is known the world over. Lloyd became *Loia* (*loh ee' ah*), a softening of his English name. The artistic Belle became *Teuila* (*tay yu ee' lah*), Bestower of Beauty. Fanny was *Tamaitai* (*tah my' ty*), High Chief Lady. Aunt Maggie was *Tamaitai Matua* (*mah tu' ah*), the Old Chief Lady. For Fanny the natives had still another name. It was *Aolele* (*ou lay' lay*), Flying Cloud. It was their smiling reference to her unfailing energy.

The residents of Vailima lived a busy life. Although Stevenson was head of the household, his day was largely occupied with writing. Lloyd, who was in his early twenties, was general superintendent. Aunt Maggie was young Austin's tutor. Joe Strong returned to the United States. Belle was housekeeper and Stevenson's secretary. Fanny, who loved the good earth, was head gardener. She worked especially hard at the cacao crop, for she hoped it would be a means to lighten her husband's need for money.

171

Meanwhile Louis had completed the travel letters which had enabled him to come to the South Seas in the first place. He finished a book, *The Wrecker*, with Lloyd. He had in mind a book to have the same characters as *Kidnapped*, which he would call *David Balfour*. When he was homesick for Edinburgh and Scotland, writing about them helped him to forget the distance between them and Vailima.

But he was not always longing for the land which he had left. Vailima was home now. His own relatives and his servants, who were his adopted children, looked to him as the head of the family. Lloyd had grown up. Stevenson knew he must write to support them all. But there was plenty of time for companionship, talk, and laughter.

Often the great fifty-foot dining hall, paneled in redwood from California, resounded with the conversation of guests from Apia and young lieutenants and midshipmen from the visiting British men-of-

172

war. Twenty guests could sit at the long mahogany table. Many times twenty guests did sit there, for Stevenson loved people.

If he had dressed carelessly as a youth, he did a right-about-face now. On formal occasions he wore a white dinner jacket, white silk shirt, black dress trousers, and gleaming patent leather shoes. He tied a scarlet sash about his slender waist. In his own words: "O a great sight!"

There were many occasions that called for formal dress — dinners in the great hall at Vailima, dances and balls down at Apia, visits to the British men-of-war. Stevenson was no longer the ragamuffin of his student days.

And in the midst of all of it, Austin was playing at war games with lead soldiers, riding pack horses down the trail, being coached by Aunt Maggie until he grew old enough to be sent away to school.

Vailima was a home. It was the center of the Stevensons' universe. There was room in it to grow, and Stevenson was growing.

CHAPTER 18

Road of the

Loving Heart

When Louis came to Samoa, the islands were a hotbed of politics. Upolu, the island where Vailima was located, was under the joint control of three foreign nations: England, Germany, and the United States. The natives were allowed to have their own king. The trouble was that they could not agree on the king. Some islanders wanted Laupepa (*lah u pay' pah*), and others wanted Mataafa (*mah tah ah' fah*).

Mataafa was the better man, but the foreign powers wanted Laupepa. Thus the natives were divided into two camps. There

175

were threats of uprisings and revolutions.

It was a serious matter for the Samoans. Stevenson learned the facts, formed his opinion, and then plunged into native politics. Although he liked Laupepa, he approved of Mataafa and said so. At length the smoldering fire broke out into open warfare. It was bloody, but it soon ended. A British warship steamed into the harbor and put an end to the fighting. Mataafa was sent away. Twenty-three of his chiefs were thrown into prison.

The sorry affair was over. But Louis did not forget his unfortunate friends. He felt that they had been treated badly. He visited them in jail. He saw that they had food and medical care. After a long time, through his efforts, they were released one by one.

One day a group of chiefs went to Vailima to see Stevenson. They were from among those who had been in prison. They wanted to thank *Tusitala* for his many kindnesses. They said they had a gift for him.

Their head chieftain stopped forward. "O friend and protector," he said "we owe

you a debt we can never repay. We realize
that the path from here down to the cross-
roads of the island is but a poor one. We
know that rains make it impassable. Therefore we desire to build you with our own
hands a road that shall last forever."

Stevenson was deeply touched. He knew that all Samoans hated roadbuilding. And here these men — chieftains, at that — were offering to build him a road as a *mea alofa* (*may' ah ah loh' fah*) — a gift of love.

He smiled at the brown-skinned natives and spoke in their own tongue. "My brothers, I accept your offer with gratitude.

You are giving me far more than I ever gave you. By all means, build it. We shall call it 'The Road of the Loving Heart.' "

The chieftains lost no time in carrying out their offer. They collected a large number of their finest and strongest young men. For weeks they worked in the tropical heat. They cut down trees. They burned under-

growth. They hauled away stumps and rocks.

When the road was completed, it was thirty feet wide and wound all the way down the mountainside. The formal opening took place with many guests, ringing speeches, and a joyful feast at the end.

A wooden signboard marked the beginning of the new road. It read:

Considering the great love of Tusitala in his loving care of us in our distress in the prison, we have therefore prepared a splendid gift. It shall never be muddy, it shall endure forever, this road that we have dug.

It was 1894 now. Stevenson was forty-four years old. He had celebrated his birthday on November 13. The Samoans wanted to give him a birthday feast. So there were gifts and native dishes and songs and speeches.

Later there was a Thanksgiving Day dinner that those present never forgot. The servants wore their plaid tartans and flowers in their hair. Together with a few American guests

from Apia, the family celebrated in true
American fashion. There was a big turkey
for Louis to carve and something that looked
like cranberry sauce. There was sweet potato
pudding. There were real American apples
from a ship that had just landed. There was
ice from the little ice machine. Ice was a
rare treat in the tropics.

Stevenson smiled the length of the board
at Fanny, who sat at the other end of the
table. He was thinking that they had come

a long way since the evening he had leaped over the low sill into the dining room at Grez and found her waiting there. Many things had happened since then: a long and seemingly hopeless courtship — Fanny's return to America — his voyage across the Atlantic to join her — poverty, illness, and the possibility of death — then marriage at last and reunion with his loved ones in England — Davos — Hyères — Bournemouth — Skerryvore — his father's death — the recrossing of the Atlantic — fame at last — a voyage to the South Sea Islands from which he had never returned — and now, at last, Vailima, the home port, with his family gathered about him.

He rose and spoke what was in his heart. He gave thanks for Fanny — "Trusty, dusky, vivid, true" — and for his mother, who was still with them. Then, looking past Lloyd and Belle, he smiled at little Austin Strong.

"Vailima is blessed, for there is a child in the house," he said.

☆ ☆ ☆

December 3 started out like any other day. For the usual length of time he dictated to Belle. His current book was *Weir of Hermiston*.

Late in the afternoon he came downstairs to read his work to Fanny, as he always did. She was sad and unhappy.

"I have a feeling that something terrible is about to happen, Louis."

"Nonsense," he answered lightly.

But he failed to cheer her. She seemed filled with anxiety.

"I'll make the mayonnaise for the salad," he told her. "Where is a bowl? I'm a wonderful chef."

He tied a big apron about his slender waist. In a moment he was busily breaking eggs and twirling the eggbeater.

Suddenly he pressed his hands to his head. "Do I look strange?" he asked in a terrifying voice.

They were the last words he ever spoke. He staggered and almost fell. With the help of a servant, Fanny got him to his grandfather's old armchair which stood in the long paneled hall.

Lloyd saddled a horse and rode madly down the mountain for a doctor. Two medical men came back with him. They only shook their heads. In a few hours, Robert Louis Stevenson was dead.

He lay in state in the great hall under the British flag that had always flown above Vailima. His faithful servants watched at his side. Word of his death went out through all the island. All night his Samoan friends

came to bid him farewell. They brought with them precious handwoven mats which had been in their families for years. These they laid over him as a token of their love.

One old chief said: "We were in prison, and he cared for us. We were sick, and he made us well. We were hungry, and he fed us. The day was no longer than his kindness. *Talofa, Tusitala* — farewell."

Stevenson had said more than once that he desired to be buried on the top of Mount Vaea high above Vailima. By dawn scores of young Samoan men had gathered with knives and axes. They said they would make a road through the jungle to the top of the mountain. They were the same men who had built the Road of the Loving Heart.

By noon the path was cleared. Stevenson's brown-skinned brothers bore him shoulder high up the steep trail. Nearly everyone on the island followed the little procession up the mountain.

At last they reached the summit. There they buried him on a small plateau which

Stevenson's grave

formed the top of the mountain. Today he rests in eternal peace high above the Pacific. A huge block of concrete covers his grave. Engraved on the stone are the thistle and the hibiscus blossom, emblems of Scotland and Samoa, together with the words of the *Requiem:*

> Under the wide and starry sky,
> Dig the grave and let me lie.
> Glad did I live and gladly die,
>   And I laid me down with a will.
>
> This be the verse you grave for me:
> *Here he lies where he longed to be;*
> *Home is the sailor, home from the sea,*
>   *And the hunter home from the hill.*

Author's Note

The people, the places, and most of the events in this book are real — so real that I just stood back and let them tell their story. For instance, I know that Robert Louis Stevenson lived as a very small boy at 17 Heriot Row in Edinburgh, Scotland. He was an only child. Because he was not strong, he spent much time indoors and even in bed. In Chapter 1, as in the other chapters, the conversations are purely imaginary — but quite possible.

There really was a toy theater and an Aunt Jane, just as there was a Cousin Bob and a Cummy, not to mention Mother and Father. (And don't forget the lamplighter.)

In real life, Robert Louis Stevenson belonged to a group of boys called the Lantern Bearers. The particular incident of which I have written is one which *might* have happened.

During his short life, he traveled on the continent of Europe, came back to Scotland, journeyed to America, where he married, returned once more to Scotland, lived in Switzerland, crossed the Atlantic again, set off with his family on a six months' cruise in the Pacific, and at last found a home in the faraway Samoan Islands. Those events and others in my book are true. The people are real people. I just tried to bring them to life for you by using a little imagination.

Stevenson was so filled with a zest for living that things happened wherever he went. I hope my book will be the beginning of a long friendship for you with him. As you grow up, you will want to read everything he wrote and learn about everything he did.

Welcome to the club of Stevenson admirers!

KATHARINE WILKIE

Some Books
by
Robert Louis Stevenson

The Black Arrow

A Child's Garden of Verses

David Balfour

Dr. Jekyll and Mr. Hyde

An Inland Voyage

Travels with a Donkey

The Silverado Squatters

The Amateur Emigrant

Kidnapped

The Master of Ballantrae

Weir of Hermiston

Prince Otto

Treasure Island

Grateful acknowledgment is made to Charles Scribner's Sons for permission to reproduce some of the poems published in the Scribner Illustrated Classics edition of *A Child's Garden of Verses.*

PIPER BOOKS

ABIGAIL ADAMS: *The President's Lady,* by Regina Z. Kelly
JOHN ALDEN: *Steadfast Pilgrim,* by Cecile Pepin Edwards
ETHAN ALLEN: *Green Mountain Hero,* by Sheldon N. Ripley
HANS CHRISTIAN ANDERSEN: *Fairy Tale Author,* by Shannon Garst
DAN BEARD: *Boy Scout Pioneer,* by Jerry Seibert
DANIEL BOONE: *Wilderness Trailblazer,* by Miriam E. Mason
KIT CARSON: *Mountain Scout,* by Donald E. Worcester
HENRY CLAY: *Statesman and Patriot,* by Regina Z. Kelly
CHRISTOPHER COLUMBUS: *Sailor and Dreamer,* by Bernadine Bailey
AMELIA EARHART: *First Lady of the Air,* by Jerry Seibert
HENRY FORD: *Maker of the Model T,* by Miriam Gilbert
BENJAMIN FRANKLIN: *First Great American,* by John Tottle
ULYSSES S. GRANT: *General and President,* by Joseph Olgin
JOHN HANCOCK: *Friend of Freedom,* by Jeannette C. Nolan
PATRICK HENRY: *Voice of Liberty,* by William Percival Jones
MATTHEW HENSON: *Arctic Hero,* by Sheldon N. Ripley
SAM HOUSTON: *Friend of the Indians,* by Joseph Olgin
HENRY HUDSON: *Explorer of the North,* by Dorothea J. Snow
THOMAS JEFFERSON: *Champion of the People,* by Joseph Olgin
JOHN PAUL JONES: *Soldier of the Sea,* by Donald E. Worcester
ABRAHAM LINCOLN: *Man of Courage,* by Bernadine Bailey
JAMES MADISON: *Statesman and President,* by Regina Z. Kelly
FERDINAND MAGELLAN: *Noble Captain,* by Katharine Wilkie
HORACE MANN: *Sower of Learning,* by Cecile Pepin Edwards
KING PHILIP: *Loyal Indian,* by Cecile Pepin Edwards
JUAN PONCE DE LEON: *First in the Land,* by Bernadine Bailey
PONTIAC: *Lion in the Forest,* by Wilma Pitchford Hays
JOHN WESLEY POWELL: *Canyon's Conqueror,* by Marian T. Place
PAUL REVERE: *Colonial Craftsman,* by Regina Z. Kelly
SACAJAWEA: *Guide to Lewis and Clark,* by Jerry Seibert
JOHN SMITH: *Man of Adventure,* by Miriam E. Mason
ROBERT LOUIS STEVENSON: *Storyteller and Adventurer,*
    by Katharine Wilkie
HARRIET TUBMAN: *Flame of Freedom,* by Frances T. Humphreville